D1459382

Just a Song at Twilight

Just a Song at Twilight

The Second Parlour Song Book

Edited and introduced by

MICHAEL R. TURNER

AND

ANTONY MIALL

MICHAEL JOSEPH

Also by Michael R. Turner

PARLOUR POETRY
THE PARLOUR SONG BOOK
with music edited by Antony Miall

First published in Great Britain by Michael Joseph Ltd
52 Bedford Square, London, WC1B 3EF
1975

ISBN 0 7181 1339 X

Filmset in Photon Imprint 11 on 12 pt by
Richard Clay (The Chaucer Press) Ltd, Bungay, Suffolk
and printed in Great Britain by
Fletcher & Son Ltd, Norwich

Preface and Acknowledgements

It was obvious even while we were compiling *The Parlour Song Book* a couple of years ago that one volume alone could not do justice to the rich hoard of Gems to be found hidden among the piles of yellowing sheet music that form a memorial to the vocal music of several generations of the Victorian middle-classes. In the first collection we selected the finest, the most representative and a few of the worst examples of the genre that were readily available to us. For *Just a Song at Twilight* we have gone further and sought out from libraries and private collections specific songs of particular fineness, importance, interest or, in just one or two cases, of horror, thus strengthening certain themes stated in the earlier book as well as filling gaps. It is for the reader and singer to judge, but we feel that this new anthology provides quite as much—if not more—pleasure for performer and audience and lifts the curtain higher still on the private life of our forbears. However, it is certainly not dependent upon the first book, and can stand alone as a Casquet of Gems of many hues.

The Introduction that follows is not a recapitulation of the essay that opened *The Parlour Song Book*, but an attempt to explain why nineteenth-century vocal composers and poets wrote as they did and how they developed their distinctive themes and styles. It also deals with two genres within the genre—comic songs and Irish ballads—that had to be left out of the previous collection, not because they were inferior to other types of song but because they needed more space than could be given them.

As before, we have to thank all those who have helped in the compilation of this volume. Particular gratitude must go to the several historians who have already surveyed the field, especially Sigmund Spaeth, whose *History of Popular Song in America* not only provided much-needed guidelines, but also a mine of beguiling detail about individual pieces and the men and women who wrote, composed and sang them. Thanks are due for the patience and perseverance shown by the staffs of the Library of the British Museum and the BBC Music Library, and also to Ralph, Molly and Miles Izzard, Bernard Stapely, Trevor Webb and Peter Miall. We are indebted to Susan Jourdain for the loan of rare sheet music from her collection to provide illustrations for several sections of this book. The Performing Rights Society gave detailed assistance in tracing copyrights, and it is entirely our responsibility if we have failed after diligent searching to discover the copyright holders of one or two pieces. To the latter we apologise. We are also grateful to the publishers whose names are listed on another page for permission to reproduce copyright works. Finally, heartfelt thanks must go to the many people who have written to us since the publication of the earlier book with information or queries that have set us on new trails of discovery.

M. R. T., A. M.

Contents

5 Hope Springs Eternal

6 The Emerald Isle

7 What Jolly Fun

8 Two's Company, *a selection of duets*

Introduction

I

Just a song at twilight, when the lights are low,
And the flick'ring shadows softly come and go,
Tho' the heart be weary, sad the day and long,
Still to us at twilight comes Love's old song,
Comes Love's old sweet song.

The words of J. Clifton Bingham set to that immortal melody by James Molloy* still weave a spell around us. Peering through the mists of a hundred years we see the gaslit family evenings mingling jollity and gentle melancholy, we see lovers yearning, lovers parting, lovers weeping a bitter tear, we see little children on their deathbeds piping a few bars of a much-loved hymn to the improvement of their sorrowing relatives, we see philanthropic ladies dispensing soup to pathetic waifs in the city street, we see stage coaches rattling down country roads in the oranges and browns of a chromolithographic dusk, we see soldiers in red, blue or grey valiantly bearing the Union Jack, the Stars and Stripes or the Stars and Bars through shot and shell, we see the Victorians as they liked to see themselves.

Ensnared by the silken threads of sentimentality it is easy for us to imagine a fragrant world that never existed. What is nostalgia to us was often in reality also nostalgia to our forbears. After all, the very first line of 'Love's Old Sweet Song' is 'Once in the dear dead days beyond recall . . .'

Scholars have drawn fascinating and sometimes surprising conclusions from word counts of Elizabethan playwrights. While the olive grove of Academe would hardly rock if revelations came from the study of parlour balladry or from proof that Claribel wrote Adelaide Proctor, a count of significant words in the one hundred and thirteen lyrics in this volume and its companion, *The Parlour Song Book*, does throw light on what the Victorians appreciated in their popular songs. There appears to be a number of key words which served as stimuli to produce mental salivation in nineteenth-century auditors. In compiling the list below, the editors have counted derivatives from principal words together with the words themselves. Thus a count of the word 'love' includes 'lover', 'loved', 'loving' and 'lub', and 'song' includes 'sang', 'sing' and 'sung', although in some cases, as with 'old', where derivatives occur very seldom, the total listed is for that single word alone. The note 'etc.' after a word in the table below indicates the inclusion of derivatives.

love, etc.	148	death, etc.	62
home	107	sweet, etc.	59
old	102	dear, etc.	46
heart, etc.	84	tear, etc.	33
mother	77	dream, etc.	31
little	64	weep, etc.	24
song, etc.	63	Heaven	19

* 'Love's Old Sweet Song' is printed in *The Parlour Song Book*.

Certainly, one would have expected 'love' to head the list, as it must do for a count of present-day lyrics, but it is followed closely and significantly by 'home'. The other traditional triggers for nostalgic response, 'old' and 'mother', score very highly, as do those emotive adjectives 'sweet' and 'little'. It is possible to understand how close 'Love's Old Sweet Song' was to Victorian tastes: the title itself comprises four of the nine most popular words. Other interesting points emerge from this count. The lachrymose character of much nineteenth-century balladry, for instance, is clearly evident. The period really was one in which people revelled in sweet sorrow: not for nothing were many songs headed by the instruction 'with melancholy expression'.

The poetry of parlour song, then, mirrors the middle-class predilection for nostalgia and sentimentality. It deluded the Victorians as much as it deludes us. Why, in this most revolutionary of centuries, should escapism so create an all-pervading aura throughout popular art that much of our view of the period is coloured by it? To ascribe it to simple reaction against the turbulence of the contemporary world is not entirely convincing. It has a close relationship to the moral earnestness that is another unique feature of the time, and music was seen as having a potent role in the battle for men's souls.

Being independent of dangerous words or suggestive graphic representation, 'Music can suggest no improper thought, and herein lies its superiority over painting and sculpture.' That was Sir Arthur Sullivan's view, and it echoed popular opinion.

II

'The laws of morality are also those of art,' declared Robert Schumann. Richard Wagner averred that music 'will never cease to be the noblest and purest of arts . . . Its inherent solemnity makes it so chaste and wonderful that it ennobles whatever comes into contact with it'. Moritz Hauptmann, the noted German professor of musical theory, if not quite so lofty was equally definite when he wrote in 1870: 'Where there is no heart there can be no music.'

There was plenty of heart in Britain and America to sustain the greatest outburst of music-making the Western world had known, and most musicians agreed with Schumann and Wagner that their art was a powerful force for good. The urge to justify entertainment by claiming the noble ends justified the pleasurable means is typically Victorian. Indeed, the more pleasurable the means the more swiftly could the moral ends be encompassed. The gospel hymns of Sankey and Moody at the end of the century used the dance rhythms and other techniques of popular song both to catch the ear of the unchurched and to sustain the enthusiasm of the converted.

The concern with morals was so intense that it had some curious side effects, especially in matters of artistic taste. Because the Germans were similarly preoccupied and had a national tendency towards regimentation and severe philosophising, the English-speaking nations found them especially admirable. Germany was the home of Luther and Protestantism, as opposed to the popishness and instability of the Latin countries, and additionally for Britain there were august Royal connections. The Reverend H. R. Haweis, amateur of the violin and author of the influential *Music and Morals*, was quite positive about the musical implications:

> . . . it is because German music has probed the humanities and sounded the depths of our nature—taught us to bring the emotional region not only into the highest activity, but also under the highest control—that we place German music in the first rank.

The Germans were eminently respectable; they were also safe. In Oscar Wilde's *The Importance of Being Earnest*, Lady Bracknell, concerned about the propriety of the programme of songs arranged by her nephew Algernon for her Saturday reception, remarks:

> I'm sure the programme will be delightful, after a few expurgations. French songs I cannot possibly allow. People always seem to think they are improper, and either look shocked, which is vulgar, or laugh which is worse. But German sounds a very respectable language, and, indeed, I believe is so.

Native English composers were bound to suffer from this Germanic sway. J. A. Fuller-Maitland, surveying the work of Edward J. Loder in *Music in the Nineteenth Century*, published in 1902, says of the song 'The Brooklet': 'It is quite certain that, had the author been German, this and many other songs would be known the world over, instead of being quite inaccessible to the ordinary person . . .' In *My Musical Life* the Reverend Haweis complained testily of the English:

> They may cultivate music, they may like it and pay for it, but they do not produce anything to be compared with the works of the great masters of the Continent. The national music is about 'Champagne Charley', 'Tommy', 'Waking the Baby', 'Grandfather's Clock' [which is in fact American—Eds.], and 'Over the Garden Wall'. It is true we have Sir Arthur Sullivan, whose compositions are always welcome; but he studied in Germany, he took the Mendelssohn scholarship at Leipsig, and therefore he may be considered, so far as music is concerned, a German to the backbone . . .

So much for the apparent Englishness of *H.M.S. Pinafore* and *The Yeomen of the Guard.* Despite the element of cultural snobbery in all this, it is impossible to escape the conclusion that one main reason why the Germans were held in high esteem was because they kept a tight rein on the emotions.

A preoccupation with restricting human appetites has been recurrent throughout history: St Paul, Savanarola, the Puritans, Dr Bowdler, Mrs Grundy and thousands of others have fought to ameliorate man's behaviour by restricting it. During the nineteenth century a dominant section of society, the new middle-classes, went even further: for the first time there was a concerted if unconscious attempt not only to bring man's appetites under control but also every innermost thought.

Until the last century the emotions of all but a small minority of the Anglo-Saxon race were very close to the surface. Men and women wept openly and unashamedly from grief or relief, shrieked in terror and quarrelled explosively quite as readily and demonstratively as peoples supposedly less phlegmatic than ourselves still do today. As the years went by, undisciplined and undignified displays were held increasingly reprehensible as the emergent bourgeoisie adopted the manners of polite society—and sentimentality started to blossom.

Social correctness has always involved formal behaviour, ceremonial and the control of emotional response. Squeeze a balloon in one direction and it swells out in another; so do the emotions. Restrict them and they manifest themselves in a different form. The conventions newly acquired by the middle-classes from their social betters demanded that while a modicum of tears were *de rigueur* in the event of a bereavement, violent exhibitions of personal grief were not: hence the emergence of the nineteenth-century funeral with its pomp and ritual to provide a surrogate.

Furthermore, in the home the traumatic effects of love, of parting, of sickness and death denied the relief of simple and immediate outburst manifested themselves over a longer period in the indulgence of the emotions in sentimental popular art, of which song was an integral part. Gradually the Victorians found there was real enjoyment to be found in polite melancholy. The wallowing in the morbid that became such a feature of the period performed much the same service as pornography does for the sexually deprived.

In America, ordinary God-fearing folk often had to erect defences against the excesses of a frontier society. A minority in the Eastern States had social pretensions and conventions not all that far from those of contemporary Europe, but both homesteaders and small-town and city dwellers in general required a sturdier and more practical code for the rough and tumble of life. This code emerged in the form of what we know as 'the protestant ethic', which held that moral behaviour was rewarded materially in this world as well as assuring an honourable place in the next. As the hazards of living were apt to strike indifferently among the good as well as the errant, it was necessary to explain the apparent failure of Providence to keep its part of the bargain. This was done by recourse to an age-old concept: that disaster was sent not only as punishment but as a lesson to the faithful. Thus the early death of an innocent child, for instance, could be used as instructive material to be pondered, and indeed, by idealising the situation, to be relished:

And when my little playmates come,
To see me laid within the tomb:
Tell them, I went to that bright land,
Where sin and sorrow never come.
And father, when you are alone,
My spirit near will ever keep.
I'll lead you to the heav'nly throne,
Now kiss me and I'll go to sleep.

As the Duchess remarked in *Alice in Wonderland*, 'Everything's got a moral, if only you can find it.' A very Victorian observation.

III

While moral constraints planted the roots of sentimentality firmly in nineteenth-century soil, it was the fertiliser of mass literacy that produced the luxuriant blossoms that amaze and sometimes amuse today. For the first time the simpler art concepts became available to a wide public. Previously only the leisured classes had a musical grounding; now there was a great explosion in musical education with the help of simplified methods including Curwen's Tonic Sol-Fa system—which was propagated as a potent means of moral improvement.

America as well as Britain was swept by the missionary zeal of the educators with their belief that music would not only soothe the savage breast of the masses but instil in it the sobering ideas of nonconformism. Music had formerly been a pleasant social accomplishment; now the additional moral attribute made it hugely popular among the respectable. In 1850 *Eliza Cook's Journal* recorded: 'female children are too ordinarily set to music whether they have an ear for it or not, because, forsooth, it is a fashionable branch of education'. Twentieth-century techniques of educational technology were foreshadowed by some of the systems of mass instruction: Logier taught classes using twenty pianos at a time played by twice that number of young ladies. E. D. Mackerness reports in *A Social History of English Music* that in 1863 a hundred and eighty thousand pupils were learning to sing in the Tonic Sol-Fa notation in Britain alone. Schools, churches, mechanics' institutes and social clubs took to choral activity enthusiastically, and it is no accident that Victorian composers were hardly considered worthy of serious consideration until they had produced at least one oratorio or sacred cantata. Music was not only taken up by the masses; it was performed in the mass. Choral performances by over a thousand voices supported by overgrown orchestras were not uncommon, and it appears from contemporary engravings that the performers on these occasions sometimes outnumbered their audiences.

However impressive the explosion, the degree of musical understanding engendered by the new methods of education was not very great. The Tonic Sol-Fa and other systems of notation replaced conventional notes, considered too rarefied a matter for ordinary minds to comprehend, with syllables and letters. Some of the methods could not even cope with key changes, and while the many thousands of proud graduates created a demand for music to perform, that music had to be simple and direct in appeal. This lack of musical sophistication coincided with a lack of literary sophistication. It was natural in these circumstances for half understood artistic concepts and partially grasped techniques to be perverted into a whole new crop of clichés. The emergent middle-classes, enthusiasts in a great age of discovery, were inheritors at their own level of a folk tradition in song that they rejected unconsciously as outdated and unacceptably coarse. These fresh acolytes of Polyhymnia selected those elements in the arts that gave them most immediate satisfaction, and applied them to the expression of contemporary social and moral ideas.

The emotions are always an essential part of the stock-in-trade of the arts, and the Victorians discovered that in song they could indulge those feelings that nonconformist restraint denied outlet in more direct fashion. The surprising thing is not that the sentimentalities of the time should have been so vulgar—the musical equivalent of the bulbosities of over-decorated Victorian furniture—but that they were frequently so fresh and charming. Admittedly, the songs in this volume are not a typical cross-section; they include some of the best (and one or two of the worst) pieces of the century and do not represent effectively the immensely dull and unremarkable flood of ballads from both the old world and the new, but the really good songs are only exceptional in being the best of their distinctive kind. They are far from being untypical in subject matter or style. One superb example is the setting of Poe's verses 'Annabelle Lee' by Henry Leslie, an Anglo-American production that is completely of its period and yet is worthy to stand high in any selection of fine songs of all times.

IV

Parlour song has had a devastatingly bad press over the years. The Reverend Haweis, who is quoted above, dismissed it as unworthy to be set against the productions of the German genius, but one of the most penetrating, though hostile, comments about the genre came from America in the early 1850s. John S. Dwight wrote in his journal of the current favourite 'Old Folks at Home':

> We wish to say that such tunes, although whistled and sung by everybody, are erroneously supposed to have taken a deep hold of the popular mind; that the charm is

> only ***skin-deep***; that they are hummed and whistled ***without musical emotion***, whistled 'for lack of thought'; that they persevere and haunt the morbidly sensitive nerves of deeply musical persons, so that they too hum and whistle them involuntarily, hating them even while they hum them; that such melodies become catching, idle habits, and are not popular in the sense of musically inspiring, but that such and such a melody ***breaks out*** every now and then, like a morbid irritation of the skin.

There has been practically no serious consideration of parlour music until this day, apart from the few histories of popular song which record, often with nostalgia, but steer clear of musical judgement. The attack, however, continues with a virulence that is rather puzzling. As recently as 1966 the eminent musical historian Dr Sydney Northcote said scathingly in his *Byrd to Britten, A Survey of English Song*, 'The revulsion against these songs is now so complete, perhaps, that it would be idle to name even the more musically meritorious . . .' and elsewhere he spoke of 'the morass of Victorian song' in which not even the faintest signs of artistic progress could be found. There is also a denunciation of one important facet of the genre by Ronald Pearson in *Victorian Popular Music* published in 1973: 'Victorian popular music reached a low with the drawing-room ballad. It was a dishonest medium, cajoling the listeners into believing that they were getting art music instead of a sticky mass of sentiment and tired melody. The most incredible thing was that composers and lyric writers were equally certain that they were producing works of art.'

It is time, surely, that this huge outburst of song should be freed from sweeping judgements both absolute and social—and usually emotional. Nineteenth-century song now requires an unbiassed approach that recognises the inadequate and meretricious for what they are—and there is plenty of both—but also identifies the real gems even if they are flawed, as many of them are in one way or another.

There is no point, though, in over-praise any more than there is in wholesale condemnation. Let us recognise that doggerel often produced genuine melodic inspiration, as in 'On the Banks of the Wabash', a fact that happens to be true of vocal music of all periods. It is only necessary to recall the utterly second-rate poetry of Schumann's *Frauenliebe und Leben* or some of the libretti happily used by Mozart. The tragedy of much Victorian song is that we can understand the words. Another fact to accept is that even superb poetry can achieve an artistic nadir in an insensitive setting, as happened with the works of many leading poets at the hands of John Blockley.

Therefore, let us not judge. Let us try to understand, and in doing so find an unexpected mine of pleasure.

If quantities of inept verse and reach-me-down settings have led to critical frigidity, they have also tended to disguise the rich variety of styles that make up Victorian song as a whole. The main types overlapped and influenced each other, but they can easily be distinguished. For a proper appreciation of parlour music it is necessary to disentangle the strands; and the main threads, with some examples drawn from this volume and from *The Parlour Song Book*, may be said to be:

- The prettied-up folk-song, equipped with new words and a tasteful arrangement, exemplified by Thomas Moore's *Irish Melodies* ('The Meeting of the Waters', 'Believe Me If All Those Endearing Young Charms', 'The Last Rose of Summer')
- Theatrical numbers from popular operas or melodramas ('Home! Sweet Home!', 'Yes, Let Me Like a Soldier Fall', 'Kathleen Mavourneen')
- The improving ballad of the 1830s and 1840s ('The Old Arm Chair', 'The Village Blacksmith')

— The genteel song of love or nostalgia ('My Pretty Jane', 'Juanita', 'Rosalie, the Prairie Flower', 'I'll Take You Home Again, Kathleen')
— The 'scena' or vigorously dramatic narrative song, a favourite with the family troupes of singers in America ('The Wreck of the Hesperus', 'The Snow Storm', 'The Death of Nelson')
— The Minstrel song of the early period using comic Negro elements ('Dixie's Land', 'The Yellow Rose of Texas')
— The later Minstrel ballad, heavily sentimental and often lachrymose ('Close the Shutters, Willie's Dead', 'Kiss Me, and I'll Go to Sleep')
— The drawing-room or art ballad, product of the industry launched by English music publishers but also vigorous in America ('Three Fishers Went Sailing', 'Anchored', 'What Are the Wild Waves Saying?' 'The Rosary')
— The hymn and gospel song
— The song of social protest ('Kingdom Coming', 'Come Home, Father', 'Father's a Drunkard and Mother is Dead')
— The output of Tin Pan Alley ('In the Baggage Coach Ahead', 'The Picture With Its Face Turned to the Wall')
— Music-hall sentimentalia, popular in lower middle-class parlours ('The Ship I Love', 'Shall I Be an Angel, Daddy?')

With a repertoire as rich and varied as this, it is vain to hope to lay down hard and fast rules about forms and tendencies. The constant cross-fertilisation between the differing genres and cultures, as well as between America and Britain, make it as hard to say whence an influence comes as to tell whither it is tending.

Basically the form of Victorian songs is ballad: that is to say the vast majority are strophic settings—one melodic strain being repeated as many times as there are verses to be set. There are, however, important exceptions and qualifications.

The refrain, an integral part of the songs of the period, varied enormously in importance from one song-type to another. In a piece like the Hon. Mrs Norton's 'Juanita' it is a mere eight bars tacked on to the end of an already complete musical exposition. In 'Daddy' by Arthur Behrend, on the other hand, it is an inseparable part of the whole and is extended in the last verse to do duty as a coda. The few through-composed songs in which the composer treats each stanza to new music usually see it wither humbly into the guise of a leitmotif such as the Captain's in 'The Wreck of the Hesperus'.

Sometimes refrains are enlarged into complete choruses. This is an unfailing characteristic of Minstrel songs and is a predominantly American feature in this period. The thirty-odd years that separate the songs of composers such as Henry Clay Work and Stephen Foster from the productions of Tin Pan Alley witness a significant development. Choruses in the earlier pieces are almost all based wholly or partially on musical material taken from the preceding verses. Ninety-nine per cent of verses end in the tonic key and are perfectly complete without them. The later school, however, finds the verse paling into insignificance beside its monolithic chorus. It is the chorus that gives every appearance of having been composed and indeed written first—for the title is almost invariably found there. The verse acts merely as a recitative and closes more often than not in the dominant key leaving the chorus that follows as the only harmonic way home.

Such songs, like those of the English music-hall, are designed as much for audience participation as for audience appreciation. We all hold our breath as we hear, 'List to my story, I'll tell it all . . .' for we know that the real song is about to begin.

It is in the relative weight given to the refrain or the chorus by the two main song cultures of England and America that one of the dichotomies of nineteenth-century song is seen. For while Hatton and Hullah were sowing the seeds of the art ballad, Harry von Tilzer and Charles K. Harris were nursing the seedlings of the vast plantation of twentieth-century popular music.

V

For reasons of space it was necessary to omit from *The Parlour Song Book* several important strains in parlour balladry. It is particularly satisfying to the editors, and, they hope, to the reader, to include two of them in this volume. They are songs of national nostalgia and comic songs.

The first group, which appears as the section 'The Emerald Isle', shows how a remarkable phenomenon of popular song that still continues to flourish emerged from rather polite beginnings into mass favour. For some reason, probably because from its shores came millions of immigrants to English factories and to American cities and open spaces, Ireland attracted attention from song-writers all through the century. A few Scottish songs were heard in the parlour, but obviously the Hibernian genius lies in folksong rather than nostalgic middle-class ballads.

The key figure in the genteel exploitation of Ireland was the prolific Dublin poet Thomas Moore, who quit his homeland to pursue his career in London, acquiring aristocratic approbation and for a time the friendship of the Prince of Wales. Until Moore's advent Irish songs had been largely those of conflict or protest; such famous pieces as the seventeenth-century 'Lilliburlero' and 'The Wearin' of the Green' of about 1798 were both concerned with the English ascendancy. Young Thomas Moore, the darling of the salons, was unconcerned with civil strife or politics. He took old folk-songs, had the tunes tidied up by a Doctor of Music, Sir John Stevenson, and wrote new and nostalgic lyrics to them. With the publication of his *Irish Melodies* in 1807 and in instalments for nearly thirty years, he was the first to strike real gold in his romantically green but unhappy native land. He mined his productive vein assiduously, accepting a hundred guineas a song from his well-satisfied publishers and stamping a number of English and Scottish traditional tunes as Irish in the process. In *Seven Centuries of Popular Song* Reginald Nettel says, 'the formula is always the same, a graceful curve of a tune to which are sung sad-sweet descriptions of scenes distant either in place or time.'

Here was the perfect prescription for the genteel, romantically inclined public of the early nineteenth century. The idiom developed as the years went by, embracing the yearning of homesick emigrants, purveying increasingly rose-tinted views of Ould Erin and its warm-hearted and engagingly simple inhabitants. Some poets and composers in the genre such as M. W. Balfe and James Molloy were Irish by birth, but many were merely opportunistic Englishmen and Americans who recognised a profitable line when they saw it. Sometimes they were so adept at the required style that their songs were popularly accepted as real Irish airs: Claribel's lilting 'Come Back to Erin' was one such. By the 'nineties the tide of mock Irishry was in full flood in New York's Tin Pan Alley, and was welcomed enthusiastically by the large immigrant segment of the population for whom distance lent enchantment. The hit songs of the decade included such genuinely enchanting ballads as 'Sweet Rosie O'Grady', ostensibly by the singer Maude Nugent but probably the work of her lyricist husband, Billy Jerome.

Irish songs were generally acceptable in any company; comic songs most decidedly were not. In certain circumstances they could be cited as the ultimate deterrent, as this passage in Jerome K. Jerome's *Three Men in a Boat* makes clear:

> I mentioned these feelings of mine to Harris, and he said he had them worse than that. He said he not only felt he wanted to kill the man . . . but that he should like to slaughter the whole of his family and all his friends and relations, and then burn down his house. This seemed to me to be going too far, and I said so to Harris; but he answered: 'Not a bit of it. Serve 'em all jolly well right, and I'd go and sing comic songs on the ruins.'

A terrible threat. For the full horror of what the comic song could do to innocent bystanders in the year 1889, one must turn again to the classic passage in *Three Men in a Boat* in which Harris attempts to deliver the First Lord's Song out of *H.M.S. Pinafore* under the illusion that he is singing the Judge's Song from *Trial by Jury*. The process reduces his accompanist to a quivering wreck and a nervous old lady has to be led from the room in tears. As 'J' the narrator remarks:

> Well, you don't look for much of a voice in a comic song. You don't expect correct phrasing or vocalisation. You don't mind if a man does find out, when in the middle of a note, that he is too high, and comes down with a jerk. You don't bother about time. You don't mind a man being two bars in front of the accompaniment, and easing up in the middle of a line to argue it out with the pianist, and then starting the line afresh. But you do expect the words.

Well, yes. Certain standards of manner and matter had to be maintained. No wonder that comic songs were regarded by all right-thinking Victorians as a plague better avoided. In his compendium of ballads, *Songs That Never Die* of 1894, the American compiler Henry Frederick Reddall is firm: '. . . those who wish to execute English "comic" songs may spare themselves any anxiety as to their voices: if they have any voice naturally, "comic" singing will soon destroy its charm, and that will not matter to them, for the last thing necessary to sing a "comic" song is the possession of a voice of any kind.' Poor Mr Reddall. He had obviously been listening to Harris.

However, it is necessary to take care in ascribing the general disfavour in which comic songs were held in respectable circles to the shortcomings of their exponents. The lower classes in Britain and America had no difficulty in laughing loud and long at each other's misfortunes or the funny habits of minorities or foreigners. They could also laugh in the face of disaster as music-hall songs show, and they had a partiality for black humour of a kind that turns the stomach even in these violent days. The self-righteous in the middle-class could not laugh in the same way: the springs of humour lie in the loss of dignity, and the preservation of earnestness and decorum was a social indicator that divided the bourgeoisie from its origins a few generations back. An elaborate edifice had been constructed. Stones through the window were not welcomed.

Human nature being what it is, humour is difficult to extinguish altogether. While there was little chance of a belly-laugh in a middle-class household, the more enlightened did encourage cerebral jokes. Puns and laboured verbal wit had a considerable vogue, and stage comedy of the mid-century erupted into a series of punning burlesques that strike us now as yawningly unfunny but provided humour of a kind.

If unseemly jocosity was discouraged in better drawing-rooms, how much more was it frowned upon on the concert platform. Comicality was left to travelling entertainers, Minstrel troupes, pantomime, burlesque (of the English, not the American variety), music-hall and vaudeville; all that was permitted as light relief was the occasional baritone rendition of a buffo song from Italian opera, or perhaps 'Simon the Cellarer', the perfect 'light humour' ballad.

Despite constant disapproval, however, cheerfulness would keep breaking in. From the 'eighties onward 'light humour' was interpreted broadly enough to embrace the patter songs from the Gilbert and Sullivan operettas, and, in Britain, in succession to jolly John L. Hatton with his 'Simon the Cellarer' and similar harmless items, such entertainers as George Grossmith senior were funny without being in the least vulgar in august drawing-rooms. Grossmith's 'See Me Dance the Polka' is gay and pointed and, what is more, could only offend the most strait-laced whose musical tastes would probably be confined to oratorio anyway.

America was, except in the more religious households, far less stiff-necked. There is a long tradition of lively, derisive Yankee humour, and most of the century's comic songs in the United States ridiculed manners, fashions, immigrants, Negroes and political rivals. Such songs, frank and unpompous, were credits to the nation's good sense, but at the risk of causing a resumption of the War of 1812, the present English editors must say that they do not find many of them very amusing now. But then the same can be said of their British equivalents: the characteristic blend of heavy puns and unashamed facetiousness reads as sadly today as no doubt the current comedy shows of television will in a century's time.

By the latter years of the nineteenth century American humour was beginning to assume some of the characteristics that have endured mightily. The family fun of 'Whist! the Bogie Man' is much more to our tastes, as are the lyrics of music-hall in England. Sadly, the rules that govern the selection of material for this volume exclude many of the period's best comic songs, for the products of music-hall and vaudeville were shunned by the respectable even though they made the palm fronds dance in a number of aristocratic salons as well as causing aspidistras to tremble in many lower middle-class parlours.

VI

Although practically all the songs in this volume were first rendered publicly by professionals, their composers expected them to be performed mostly by amateurs. Sheet music was bought in huge quantities in the last century in much the same way as records are bought now.

Today's professionalism may be a dead hand on amateur performance. The singer in the Victorian home had no records to provide a standard; the concert platform or the stage was a rosy memory and not a reproach. The amateur violinist could saw away without the fear of his technique being compared invidiously to recorded evidence of Joachim's abilities, and the lady singer could warble 'Three Fishers Went Sailing' undeterred by any possibility of reference to the tones of Madame Sterling captured on vinyl.

Naturally, there are countless thousands undiscouraged by ready access to professional performances, and many of them aspire to the highest standards. All the same, the tradition of making music in the home has declined significantly as mechanical means of entertainment have gradually taken over. There is now a certain diffidence in launching into song, and the amateur with only modest accomplishments is seen as faintly ridiculous, largely because he is often tackling something ambitious without the equipment to succeed. The songs in this book impose few such handicaps on the tyro: they were originally written with amateur performance in mind and are generally well within the range of limited vocal or pianistic techniques. An amateur orchestra grappling with Britten or Copeland is at a disadvantage because it is bound to fall short in the interpretation of highly sophisticated professional music; the singer of parlour ballads is attempting something completely within his grasp.

It may be that there is not the same satisfaction in reaching the top of a hill as there is in falling off the North Face of the Eiger, but there is still enormous pleasure to be gained from achieving modest aims. Parlour songs cannot be appreciated on the page. They must be performed, for then they blossom and even their outdated sentiments acquire a new validity. The editors of this volume have the hope that by providing access to some much-neglected Gems they will open a door to a treasure house of enjoyment—and a fresh appreciation of how our forefathers saw the world about them.

Garden of Girls

To Anthea

Written by ROBERT HERRICK

Composed by JOHN L. HATTON

Allegro

f

1. Bid me to live, and I will live, Thy Pro-test-ant to be; Or bid me love, and I will give A lov-ing heart to thee, A heart as soft, a heart as kind, A heart as sound and free, As in the whole world thou canst find, That heart I'll give to

dim.

thee.
cresc.
dim.
2. Bid that heart stay, and it will stay To hon-our thy decresc.
f
cree; Or bid it lan-guish quite a-way, And't shall do so for
dim.
sempre p
thee. Bid me to weep, and I will weep, While I have eyes to
see, And hav-ing none, yet I will keep A heart to weep for
cresc.

thee. 3. Bid me des-paire, and I'll des-paire, Un-der that cy-presse
tree, Or bid me die, and I will dare E'en death, to die for
cresc.
cresc.
thee! Thou art my life, my love, my heart, The
sempre f
cresc. e molto
ve-ry eyes of me! And hast com-mand of ev-'ry part, To
con passione
ff
rall.
live and die for thee!
colla voce
a tempo
Ped.

To Anthea

1. Bid me to live, and I will live,
   Thy Protestant to be;
   Or bid me love, and I will give
   A loving heart to thee,
   A heart as soft, a heart as kind,
   A heart as sound and free,
   As in the whole world thou canst find,
   That heart I'll give to thee.

2. Bid that heart stay, and it will stay
   To honour thy decree;
   Or bid it languish quite away,
   And't shall do so for thee.
   Bid me to weep, and I will weep,
   While I have eyes to see,
   And having none, yet I will keep
   A heart to weep for thee.

3. Bid me despaire, and I'll despaire,
   Under that cypresse tree,
   Or bid me die, and I will dare
   E'en death, to die for thee!
   Thou art my life, my love, my heart,
   The very eyes of me!
   And hast command of ev'ry part,
   To live and die for thee!

It is one of the curiosities of Victorian song that the piece that is arguably the most mellifluous of the period should have a lyric by an irreverent Reverend gentleman of two centuries earlier. Closer inspection of the poem, however, reveals elements consistently present throughout the history of parlour song: a kind heart with a readiness to languish away, a tendency to easy tears, and a willingness to be laid under a sad cypress. No wonder is it that, given a lovely musical setting, it should have become a favourite all through the century.

This most popular of Hatton's songs owes much stylistically to Schumann whose songs he had edited for English consumption. Even so, it is still an extremely fresh composition and one that richly deserves space in any collection of the best songs of the nineteenth century from the best composers, although it would be tactful, perhaps, to leave a space between it and Schumann's 'Ich grolle nicht'.

The poet Robert Herrick (1591–1674) was the son of a London goldsmith and for six years he was apprenticed to that craft. He fell in with the band of poets that surrounded Ben Jonson and after graduating at Cambridge led a fashionable literary life. Forced to adopt the only secure occupation open to one both educated and indigent, Herrick took Holy Orders and was appointed incumbent of a Devon parish. Lonely and surrounded only by his spaniel, his pet lamb, his cat, goose, cock, hen, favourite pig, his devoted maid Prue, obnoxious neighbours and puzzled parishioners, he returned to poetry, producing some twelve hundred pieces published in his volume 'Hesperides'. Ejected from his living by the Puritans, he returned rejoicing to London and vowed to spend the rest of his days there. Nonetheless, with the Restoration he went back to his parish and, no doubt thoroughly disgruntled, died there. He appears to have been something of a rascal, and it is generally agreed that his hedonistic and pagan verse is a good deal more impressive than his religious. Many of his songs were set to music in his own time, and as well as 'To Anthea' his 'Cherry Ripe', composed by Charles Edward Horn, enjoyed great popularity in Victorian parlours.

John Liptrot Hatton (1809–1886) had a rudimentary musical education; he was mostly self-taught. This did not deter him and he eventually produced two cathedral services, eight anthems and a mass, an operetta, two operas and a hundred and fifty songs, some of the latter under the *nom de plume* of Czapek. It was, however, as an entertainer that Hatton achieved most contemporary acclaim. One of the first exponents of 'songs at the piano', he was a man of parts, lecturing, singing, playing the pianoforte and organ, conducting oratorio and singing the leading role the while. Perhaps because of these rather diverse activities he is now underestimated as a musician. He was responsible for much skilful editing of songs (*Songs of England* was his work) and was able to sustain a highish level of inspiration despite his butterfly approach to music. He toured America more than once, and there he sang a song called 'Sleigh-Ride' with bells tied to his legs like a morris man. One of his most admired ballads was 'Simon the Cellarer' which appears on page 224 of this collection. Hatton seems to have been a most attractive and jolly personage. One lady admirer so far forgot herself as to compare his head to 'a boiled egg with a fringe round it'. It is in character that he should have said of Bach, whose music he loved, 'That old fellow is my comforter.'

Juanita

Written and composed by the HON. MRS NORTON

moun - tain,
Breaks the day too soon!
In thy dark eyes' splen - dour Where the warm light
loves to dwell, Wea - ry looks, yet ten - der,
slower
Speak their fond fare - well!
a tempo
Ni - ta! Jua - ni - ta!
colla voce
mf

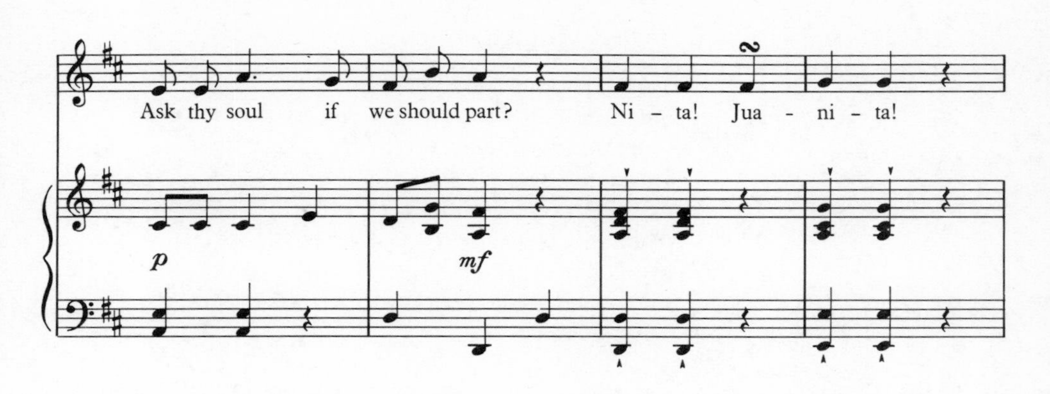
Ask thy soul if we should part?
Ni – ta! Jua - ni – ta!
p
mf

tenderly
slen.
Lean thou on my heart!
colla voce
mf a tempo

f

D.C.

Juanita

1. Soft o'er the fountain,
   Ling'ring falls the southern moon;
   Far o'er the mountain,
   Breaks the day too soon!
   In thy dark eyes' splendour
   Where the warm light loves to dwell,
   Weary looks, yet tender,
   Speak their fond farewell!

   Nita! Juanita!
   Ask thy soul if we should part.
   Nita! Juanita!
   Lean thou on my heart!

2. When in thy dreaming,
   Moons like these shall shine again,
   And daylight beaming,
   Prove thy dreams are vain.
   Wilt thou not, relenting,
   For thine absent lover sigh,
   In thy heart consenting
   To a pray'r gone by?

   Nita! Juanita!
   Let me linger by thy side!
   Nita! Juanita!
   Be my own fair bride!

Supposedly a Spanish romance, 'Juanita' makes only a token obeisance to Iberian character in its mention of the southern moon and dark eyes. The music has no Spanish feeling at all. This is one of the Hon. Mrs Norton's several contributions to English balladry: a charming and naïve melody with a rippling accompaniment which if played with a light enough touch enhances without impinging. This is one song that really cries out for a square piano with its bright yet ladylike tone.

Caroline Elizabeth Sarah Norton, née Sheridan (1808–1877), later Lady Stirling-Maxwell, had the advantage of literary ancestry: her grandfather was the playwright Richard Brinsley Sheridan. A woman of great talents, fire, personality and courage, she needed all these attributes to survive a stormy married life with the Honourable George Norton, a Commissioner of Bankruptcy who allowed his wife to support him. Her experiences led her to fight for an improvement in women's and children's legal rights. Her poems often did duty as bullets in the battle, and she was instrumental in changing the law for the better. After the death of her husband with whom she engaged in lengthy and acrimonious litigation, she married a baronet but died soon afterwards. Her head-strong romantic character won her celebrity in her day, but practically everything that poured from her prolific pen has been totally forgotten. 'The Arab's Farewell to his Steed', which appears in this book on page 94, is one of the few pieces of hers remembered today.

Rosalie, the Prairie Flower

Written and composed by G. F. WURZEL (G. F. ROOT)

And a creep-ing vine Loves a-round its porch to twine;
In that peace-ful dwell-ing was a love-ly child,
With her blue eyes beam-ing soft and mild,
And the wa-vy ring-lets of her flax-en hair,
Float-ing in the sum-mer air.
mf
Fair as a li-ly, joy-ous and free,
mf stacc.

Rosalie, the Prairie Flower

p
home was she. Ev - 'ry one who knew her,
home was she. Ev - 'ry one who knew her,
home was she. Ev - 'ry one who knew her,
home was she. Ev - 'ry one who knew her,
Repeat pp
felt the gen - tle pow'r Of Ros - a - lie the prai - rie flow'r.
felt the gen - tle pow'r Of Ros - a - lie the prai - rie flow'r.
felt the gen - tle pow'r Of Ros - a - lie the prai - rie flow'r.
felt the gen - tle pow'r Of Ros - a - lie the prai - rie flow'r.
sf

Rosalie, the Prairie Flower

1. On the distant prairie,
Where the heather wild,
In its quiet beauty lived and smiled,
Stands a little cottage,
And a creeping vine
Loves around its porch to twine;
In that peaceful dwelling was a lovely child,
With her blue eyes beaming soft and mild,
And the wavy ringlets of her flaxen hair,
Floating in the summer air.

Fair as a lily, joyous and free,
Light of that prairie home was she.
Ev'ry one who knew her, felt the gentle pow'r
Of Rosalie the prairie flow'r.

CHORUS: Fair as a lily, joyous and free, etc.

2. On that distant prairie,
When the days were long,
Tripping like a fairy, sweet her song,
With the sunny blossoms,
And the birds at play,
Beautiful and bright as they;
When the twilight shadows gather'd in the west,
And the voice of nature sunk to rest,
Like a cherub kneeling seem'd the lovely child,
With her gentle eyes so mild.

Fair as a lily, joyous and free,
Light of that prairie home was she.
Ev'ry one who knew her, felt the gentle pow'r
Of Rosalie the prairie flow'r.

CHORUS: Fair as a lily, joyous and free, etc.

Georg Friedrich Wurzel was the pseudonym and literal translation of George Frederick Root who obviously thought at the beginning of his musical career that a German name stood more chance of success with a snobbish American public. He was as calculating in his financial arrangements: he wanted more than the hundred dollars offered by his publisher for the copyright, but accepted a royalty that brought him over three thousand. No wonder he became a publisher himself.

Root manages to chop up the sense of his verses (one could hardly call them poetry) pretty effectively in his setting, but even the purist of purists must forgive him for the sake of the charming melody and for the sake of the abrupt, utterly winning change to the relative minor for two bars of the chorus.

Born in Sheffield, Mass., George Frederick Root (1820–1895) studied in Boston and Paris. He helped Lowell Mason, the pioneer in musical education, and established in 1853 the New York Normal Institute to train music teachers using Mason's methods.

Moving to Chicago he joined the music publishers Root & Cady, founded by his brother and Charles M. Cady, but kept up his teaching until his death. One of the prolific and successful American song-writers of the mid-century and beyond, he had his greatest period during the Civil War when he composed such stirring ballads as 'The Battle Cry for Freedom' with its famous call, 'Rally round the flag, boys!', 'There's Music in the Air, Boys', 'Tramp, Tramp, Tramp' and the lugubrious 'Just Before the Battle, Mother'. With 'Rosalie' of 1855 he had perhaps his biggest hit, but he also had his serious side as a composer and produced many hymns and several cantatas including *The Pilgrim Fathers*.

Alice, Where Art Thou?

Written by WELLINGTON GUERNSEY

Composed by JOSEPH ASCHER

winds sigh - ing by me, Cool - ing my fe-ver'd brow; The
stream flows as ev – er, Yet A - lice where art thou! One
year back this e – ven, And thou wert by my side,
And thou wert by my side,
Vow - ing to love me, One

year past this e - ven, And thou wert by my side,
p
ff
Vow - ing to love me, A-lice, what - e'er might betide.
dolce
1st Verse
2nd Verse
2. The
rit.

Alice, Where Art Thou?

1. The birds sleeping gently,
   Sweet Lyra gleameth bright;
Her rays tinge the forest,
   And all seems glad tonight,
The winds sighing by me,
   Cooling my fever'd brow;
The stream flows as ever,
   Yet Alice where art thou!
One year back this even,
   And thou wert by my side,
   And thou wert by my side,
Vowing to love me,
   One year past this even
And thou wert by my side,
   Vowing to love me, Alice, whate'er might betide.

2. The silver rain falling,
   Just as it falleth now;
And all things slept gently,
   Ah! Alice where art thou!
I've sought thee by lakelet,
   I've sought thee on the hill,
And in the pleasant wild-wood,
   When winds blow cold and chill;
I've sought thee in forest,
   I'm looking heav'nward now,
   I'm looking heav'nward now,
Oh! there, 'mid the starshine,
   I've sought thee in forest,
I'm looking heav'nward now,
   Oh! there amid the starshine, Alice, I know art thou.

'Alice, Where Art Thou?' manages to combine the romanticism of a love song with the melancholia of an elegy, which made it, in the early 'sixties, one of the most popular of mid-Victorian ballads. It is not surprising that it attracted some ridicule and the inevitable coarse parodies. Lyra, of the second line, is a Northern constellation. The musically literate will relish the statement of the melody beneath the singer's held notes, 'Vowing to love me', a very dramatic and operatic device.

Born in Ireland, Wellington Guernsey (1817–1855) was a soldier and war-correspondent as well as a composer, poet and librettist. As an officer and journalist he fought in and reported most of the 'little' Victorian wars, travelled widely in the Americas, and, as an engineer in Paraguayan military service, served *against* the United States and Brazil. As a song-writer, he produced, among many other ballads, 'I'll Hang my Harp on a Willow Tree' and 'I'll Think of Thee'. He offered 'Alice, Where Art Thou?' in manuscript to several music publishers for £5 and had it refused by all. It eventually sold many hundreds of thousands of copies.

The composer, Joseph Ascher (1829–1869), is only known for this one song. Of Dutch origin, he lived mostly in England. He studied music under Moscheles and was for a time Court pianist to the Empress Eugenie in Paris. Riotous living wrecked his life.

Sweet Genevieve

Written by GEORGE COOPER

Composed by HENRY TUCKER

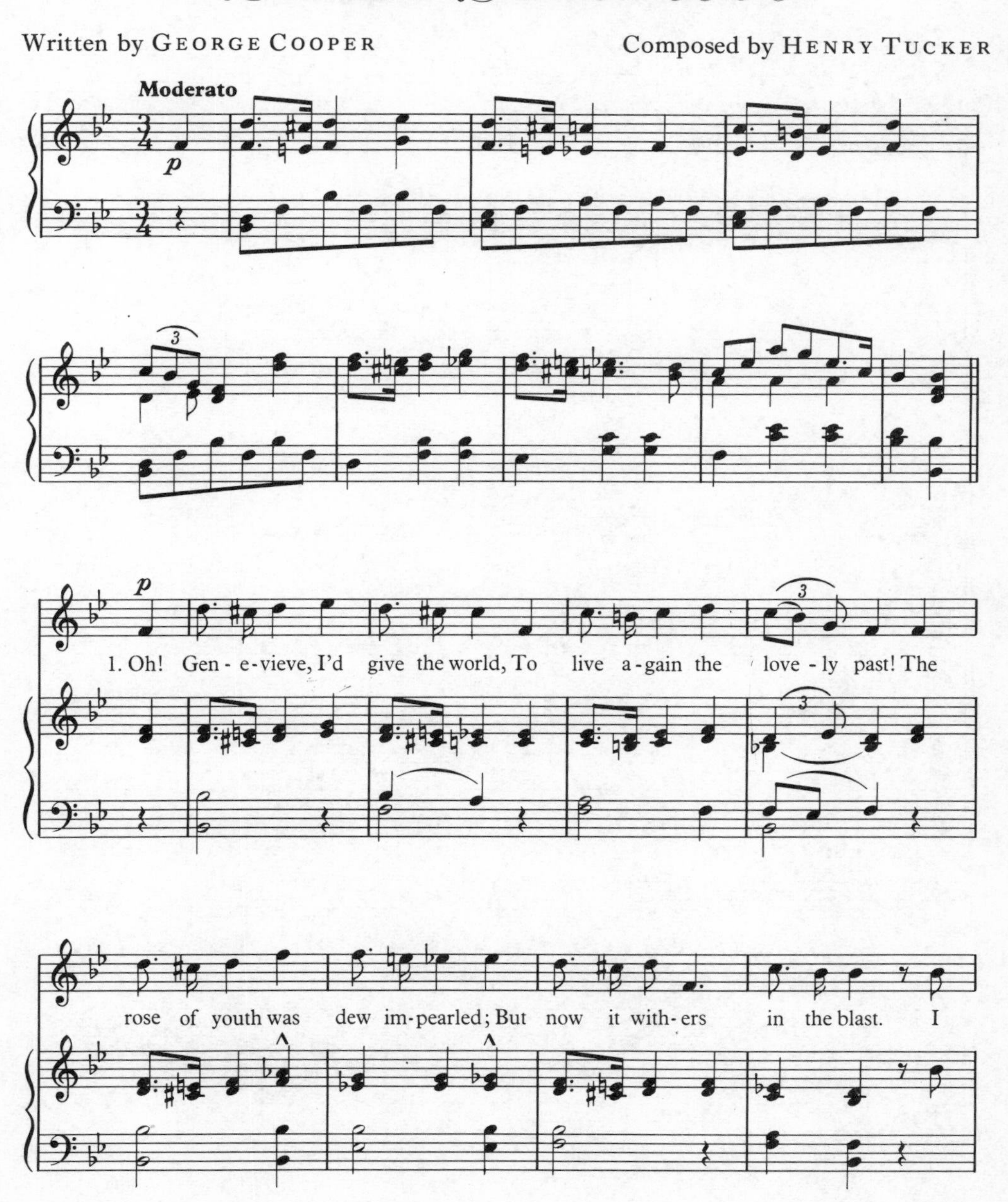

see thy face in ev'-ry dream, My wak-ing thoughts are full of thee; Thy
glance is in the star-ry beam That falls a-long the Sum-mer sea.
colla voce
CHORUS
Oh! Gen - e-vieve, Sweet Gen - e - vieve, The days may come, the
Oh! Gen - e-vieve, Sweet Gen - e - vieve, The days may come, the
Oh! Gen - e-vieve, Sweet Gen - e - vieve, The days may come, the
Oh! Gen - e-vieve, Sweet Gen - e - vieve, The days may come, the

days may go, But still the hands of mem'-ry weave The
days may go, But still the hands of mem'-ry weave The
days may go, But still the hands of mem'-ry weave The
days may go, But still the hands of mem'-ry weave The
colla voce

CODA ad lib.
bliss - ful dreams of long a - go. Oh! Gen - e - vieve.
bliss - ful dreams of long a - go. Oh! Gen - e - vieve.
bliss - ful dreams of long a - go. Oh! Gen - e - vieve.
bliss - ful dreams of long a - go. Oh! Gen - e - vieve.

Sweet Genevieve

1. Oh! Genevieve, I'd give the world,
   To live again the lovely past!
 The rose of youth was dew impearled;
   But now it withers in the blast.
 I see thy face in ev'ry dream,
   My waking thoughts are full of thee;
 Thy glance is in the starry beam
   That falls along the Summer sea.

CHORUS: Oh! Genevieve,
 Sweet Genevieve,
 The days may come, the days may go,
 But still the hands of mem'ry weave
 The blissful dreams of long ago.
   Oh! Genevieve!

2. Fair Genevieve, my early love,
   The years but make thee dearer far!
 My heart shall never, never rove:
   Thou art my only guiding star.
 For me the past has no regret
   Whate'er the years may bring to me;
 I bless the hour when first we met,
   The hour that gave me love and thee!

CHORUS: Oh! Genevieve, etc.

Although designed to draw tears in the parlour, during most of its career, as Maurice Willson Disher has pointed out in *Victorian Song*, it drew tears in the bar parlour. Genevieve is one of a select band of ladies hymned by lachrymose topers. Her sisters include Sweet Adeline in America and Nellie Dean in England—both, incidentally, fathered by the same American composer, Harry Armstrong, in 1903 and 1906 respectively.

A glance at the music suggests why the piece was favoured in places where they drink. The dying fall occurs in practically every phrase, and the ubiquitous pause marks bear witness to the emotional conception of the song.

The real Genevieve was the wife of the lyricist and songwriter George Cooper (?–1929) and she died soon after they were married. The song is a heartfelt if maudlin expression of his grief. Cooper was perennially short of money and was apt to sell his copyrights outright. He parted with 'Sweet Genevieve' (of 1869) for five dollars to the composer.

Henry Tucker (1826?–1882?) was in business as a song-writer for some forty years from the middle 'fifties onwards. The two Civil War ballads 'Weeping, Sad and Lonely' and 'Dear Mother, I've Come Home to Die', also by Tucker, are in *The Parlour Song Book.*

Annabelle Lee

Written by EDGAR ALLAN POE

Composed by HENRY LESLIE

Allegretto

p

1. It was

p dolce

ma - ny and ma - ny a year___ a - go, In a King - dom by___ the

sea, That a mai - den there lived, whom you may know By the

cres - - - cen - - do

name of An - na-belle Lee;_______ And this mai-den she lived with no

cres - - - cen - - do

f
o - ther thought Than to love and be loved by me.
f
p
Con espress.
2. I was a child and
p
she was a child, In this King - dom by the sea, But we
f
loved with a love that was more than love I and my An - na-belle
f
cres - - - - cen - do
Lee; With a love that the wing - èd se-raphs of Hea - ven
cres - - - - cen - do

f
co-vet-ed her and me.
f
p
3. And this was the rea - son that, long a - go, In this
p
King - dom by the sea, A wind blew out of a
Più mosso ed Agitato
cloud, chil - ling My beau - ti-ful An - na-belle Lee;
So that her high - born kins - men came, and bore her a - way from

me
To shut her up in a se - pulchre In this
King - dom by the sea.
My beau - ti-ful An - na-belle
Lee.
My beau - ti-ful An - na-belle Lee.
p
rall.
dim.
tempo primo
4. But the moon ne - ver beams with-out bring-ing me dreams Of the
p

cres – – – – cen –
beau - ti-ful An - na-belle Lee; And the stars ne - ver rise but I
cres – – – – cen –
– do
f
feel the bright eyes Of the beau - ti-ful An - na - belle Lee; And so
– do

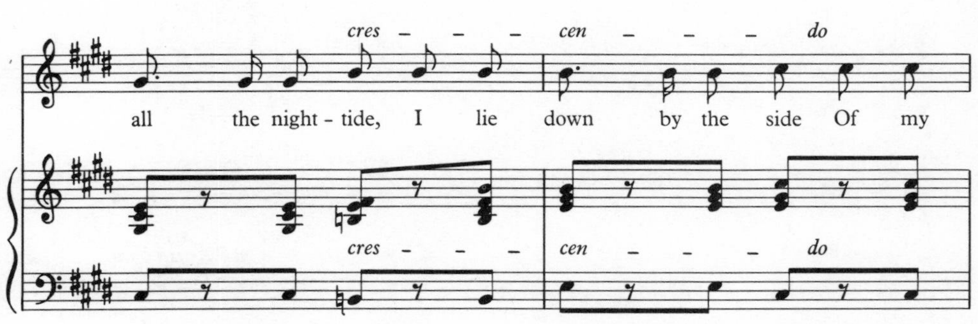
cres – – – cen – – – do
all the night - tide, I lie down by the side Of my
cres – – – cen – – – do

f
dim.
dar - ling, my dar - ling, my life and my bride; In her
f
dim.

se - pul - chre there by the sea In her
tomb by the sound - ing sea.
My
beau - ti-ful An-na - belle Lee,
My
beau - ti - ful An - na - belle Lee.
p
f
rit.

Annabelle Lee

1. It was many and many a year ago,
   In a Kingdom by the sea,
   That a maiden there lived, whom you may know
   By the name of Annabelle Lee;
   And this maiden she lived with no other thought
   Than to love and be lovèd by me.

2. I was a child and she was a child,
   In this Kingdom by the sea,
   But we loved with a love that was more than love—
   I and my Annabelle Lee;
   With a love that the wingèd seraphs of Heaven
   Coveted her and me.

3. And this was the reason that long ago,
   In this Kingdom by the sea,
   A wind blew out of a cloud, chilling
   My beautiful Annabelle Lee;
   So that her high-born kinsmen came
   And bore her away from me
   To shut her up in a sepulchre
   In this Kingdom by the sea.

4. But the moon never beams without bringing me dreams
   Of the beautiful Annabelle Lee;
   And the stars never rise but I feel the bright eyes
   Of the beautiful Annabelle Lee;
   And so, all the night-tide, I lie down by the side
   Of my darling, my darling, my life and my bride;
   In her sepulchre there by the sea—
   In her tomb by the sounding sea.
   My beautiful Annabelle Lee,
   My beautiful Annabelle Lee.

This magnificent setting of Poe's verse both complements and transcends the simplicity of the poem, exploring the implied depths of feeling in an exquisite display of compositional technique. From the gentle opening flow of the *siciliano* rhythm, through the agony of the third verse to the ecstatic reiteration of 'My beautiful Annabelle Lee', the song moves to an artistically and emotionally satisfying conclusion having said all there is to be said. Leslie was fairly cavalier with Poe's original. Two whole verses are omitted, there are alterations to the remainder and the poet's Annabel gains an '-le' to her name. On the whole, however, the composer tidied up a somewhat rambling and repetitive piece of writing. There were other settings; one by E. F. Falconnet was published in 1872.

Edgar Allan Poe (1809–1849), born in Boston, Mass., was the son of an actor and actress who left him orphaned at the age of two. His foster-father John Allen, a wealthy tobacco exporter, educated him in America and England. Notably precocious, Poe addressed his early effusions to local schoolgirls. He attended the University of Virginia where he became secretly engaged. His fiancée's parents found out and hurriedly married their daughter off to a more respectable member of society, for by now Poe was gambling and developing his fatal partiality for strong liquors. Having run away from his foster-parents, he published a book of poems in Boston and, almost destitute, joined the army. John Allen got him into West Point. He was expelled. More poems followed; he wrote stories, became a journalist and married his thirteen-year-old cousin, Virginia. His mother-in-law was to prove a sheet-anchor through the periods of poverty, Virginia's ill-health (she burst a blood-vessel while singing and contracted consumption), intoxication, affaires and sporadic success that now composed his life. His writings, as evidenced in his famous *Tales of the Grotesque and Arabesque*, touched the heights of gothick romanticism and plumbed the depths of horror and despair. At the last, his rush downhill was precipitate and despite joining the Sons of Temperance he died in a drunken coma. His irregular life produced the kind of delighted shock in American parlours that Byron caused in England; the Victorians always liked to have dreadful examples to exhibit to their children.

Henry David Leslie (1822–1896) owes the shreds of reputation remaining to him to his work in the choral movement in Britain. He began his musical career as a cellist, becoming secretary of the Amateur Musical Society. He took over a choir formed to sing madrigals, gave it his own name, and enlarged it to two hundred and forty voices. It won an international prize in Paris. Leslie was also a busy composer of opera, oratorio, instrumental music and songs. As *Grove's Dictionary of Music and Musicians* puts it succinctly, 'They are not now considered important.'

Sweet Marie

Written by Cy Warman — Composed by Raymon Moore

yet I dare not tell sweet Mar - ie. When I
hold your hand in mine, sweet Ma - rie, A
feel - ing most div - ine comes to me; All the
world is full of spring, Full of warb - lers on the wing, And I

list - en while they sing sweet Mar - ie.
CHORUS
Come to me, sweet Mar-ie, sweet Mar - ie, come to me; Not be -
f
cause your face is fair, love, to see, But your soul, so pure and sweet, Makes my
D.C.
hap - pi-ness com plete; Makes me falt - er at your feet, sweet Mar - ie.

Sweet Marie

1. I've a secret in my heart, sweet Marie;
   A tale I would impart love to thee.
 Ev'ry daisy in the dell knows my secret, knows it well,
   And yet I dare not tell sweet Marie.
 When I hold your hand in mine, sweet Marie,
   A feeling most divine comes to me;
 All the world is full of spring,
 Full of warblers on the wing,
   And I listen while they sing sweet Marie.

CHORUS: Come to me, sweet Marie, sweet Marie, come to me;
 Not because your face is fair, love, to see,
 But your soul, so pure and sweet,
 Makes my happiness complete;
 Makes me falter at your feet, sweet Marie.

2. In the morn when I awake, sweet Marie,
   Seems to me my heart will break, love, for thee.
 Ev'ry wave that shakes the shore seems to sing it o'er and o'er,
   Seems to say that I adore sweet Marie.
 When the sunset tints the west, sweet Marie,
   And I sit down to rest, love, with thee;
 Ev'ry star that studs the sky,
 Seems to stand and wonder why,
   They're so dimmer than your eye, sweet Marie.

CHORUS: Come to me, sweet Marie, etc.

There is something of the folksong in the simple, obvious words and the setting. They were certainly not aimed at a sophisticated public.

A prodigious favourite of 1893 in America, 'Sweet Marie' began life as a poem by the newspaperman Cy Warman (1855–1914), written to hymn his wife, Myrtle Marie. Warman was variously a farmer, railroad worker, journalist and writer of easy, facile verse. This latter ability won him the sobriquet of 'the bard of the Rockies'. He wrote many books on the iron way with titles like *Snow on the Headlight* and *The Last Spike.* Warman was in the West for his health, goes the story, when he showed his little poem to Raymon Moore, leading singer in a black-face Minstrel show in Denver. Moore was much taken with the piece, composed a setting that owes something to the earlier song 'Baby Mine' by Charles Mackay and Harrison Millard, and performed the song in Cleveland. It flopped. There was a row with the management and Moore resigned from the company. He was replaced by Charles Hopper who surreptitiously rehearsed the same song and without permission put it into the show at Pittsburgh where it was an immediate success and burgeoned into a national hit.

A Life on the Ocean Wave

My lov'd Lot on the Shore

The Wreck of the Hesperus

Written by HENRY WADSWORTH LONGFELLOW/Composed by JOHN L. HATTON

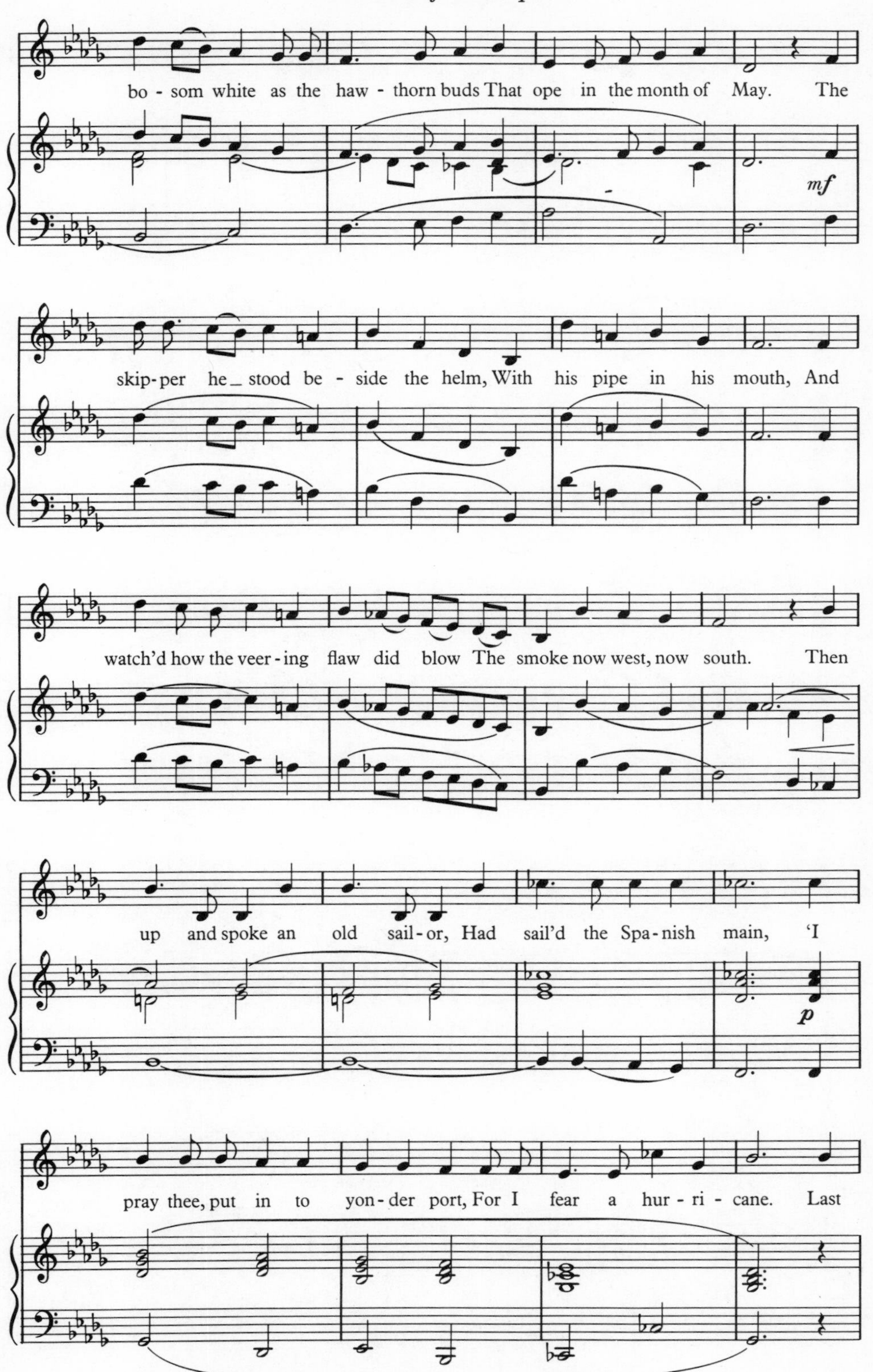

bo - som white as the haw - thorn buds That ope in the month of May. The
mf
skip-per he _ stood be - side the helm, With his pipe in his mouth, And
watch'd how the veer - ing flaw did blow The smoke now west, now south. Then
up and spoke an old sail - or, Had sail'd the Spa - nish main, 'I
p
pray thee, put in to yon - der port, For I fear a hur - ri - cane. Last

night the moon had a gold - en ring, But to - night no moon we see.' The
mf
skip-per he blew a whiff from his pipe, And a scorn - ful laugh laugh'd
he.
f
Down
came the storm, and smote a - main The
ves - sel in its strength; She
furioso

shud-der'd and paus'd like a fright - ed steed, Then
leap'd her ca - ble's length.
sf
sf
sf
sf
'Come hi-ther! come hi-ther! my lit-tle daugh-ter, And
p
do not trem-ble so, For I can wea-ther the rough-est gale That.
mf

ev-er the wind did blow.'
sf
p
sf
'Dear father! I hear the church bell ring, Oh, say what may it
sf
pp
sostenuto
sf
be?' ''Tis a fog bell_ on a rock-bound coast, We must
sf
mf
sf
steer for the o-pen sea.'
sf
sf
sf
'Dear fa-ther! I see a gleam-ing light O
sf
sf
sf
sf
sf
sf
sf
8

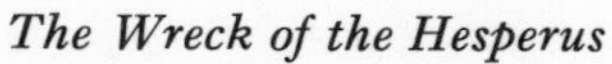

ad lib.
say what may it be?' But the fa - ther an-swer'd nev-er a word, A
8
sf
ff
pp colla voce
a tempo
fro - zen corpse was he. Lash'd to the helm all
a tempo
cresc.
stiff and stark, With his pale face to the skies; The
cresc.
lan - tern gleam'd thro' the fall - ing snow On his fix'd and glas - sy
ff
dim.
più lento
eyes. Then the maid - en clasp'd her
riten.
pp più lento

hands, and pray'd That sav - ed she might be; And she thought of
Him who still'd the waves On the lake of Ga - li - lee. But
a tempo
fast thro' the mid - night dark and drear, Thro' the
a tempo
cresc.
molto
whist - ling sleet and snow, Like a
sheet - ed ghost, the bark swept on To the reef of "Nor - man's
ff
cresc.

Woe."
sf furioso
Her ratt - ling shrouds, all
sheath'd in ice, With the masts went by the board;
Like a
sf
ves-sel of glass she stove and sank, Ho! Ho! the break-ers
sf ten.
sf ten.
sf ten.
roar'd!
8
ff
8

Andante
At day-break on the bleak sea
p
rall. e dim.
p
beach A fish-er-man stood a - ghast, To see the form of a
p
8
maid-en fair Float by on a drift-ing mast. The salt sea was fro-zen
8

on her breast, The salt tears in her eyes; And her stream-ing hair, like the
brown sea-weed, On the waves did fall and rise. Such was the wreck of the
mf
Adagio
Hes-pe-rus, In the mid-night and the snow! Oh! save us all from a
death like this, On the reef of 'Nor-man's Woe.'

The Wreck of the Hesperus

It was the schooner Hesperus,
 That sail'd in the wint'ry sea,
And the skipper had ta'en his little daughter
 To bear him company.

Blue were her eyes, as the fairy flax,
 Her cheeks like the dawn of day,
And her bosom white as the hawthorn buds
 That ope in the month of May.

The skipper he stood beside the helm,
 With his pipe in his mouth,
And watch'd how the veering flaw did blow
 The smoke now west, now south.

Then up and spoke an old sailor,
 Had sailed the Spanish Main,
'I pray thee, put into yonder port,
 For I fear a hurricane.

Last night the moon had a golden ring,
 But tonight no moon we see.'
The skipper he blew a whiff from his pipe,
 And a scornful laugh laugh'd he.

Down came the storm, and smote amain
 The vessel in its strength;
She shudder'd and paus'd like a frighted steed,
 Then leap'd her cable's length.

'Come hither! come hither! my little daughter,
 And do not tremble so,
For I can weather the roughest gale
 That ever the wind did blow.'

'Dear father! I hear the church bell ring,
 Oh say what may it be?'
' 'Tis a fog bell on a rock-bound coast,
 We must steer for the open sea.'

'Dear father! I see a gleaming light
 O say what may it be?'
But the father answer'd never a word,
 A frozen corpse was he.

Lash'd to the helm all stiff and stark,
With his pale face to the skies;
The lantern gleam'd thro' the falling snow
On his fix'd and glassy eyes.

Then the maiden clasp'd her hands, and pray'd
That saved she might be;
And she thought of Him who still'd the waves
On the lake of Galilee.

But fast thro' the midnight dark and drear,
Thro' the whistling sleet and snow,
Like a sheeted ghost, the bark swept on
To the reef of 'Norman's Woe'.

Her rattling shrouds, all sheath'd in ice,
With the masts went by the board;
Like a vessel of glass she stove and sank,
Ho! Ho! the breakers roar'd!

At daybreak on the bleak sea beach
A fisherman stood aghast,
To see the form of a maiden fair
Float by on a drifting mast.

The salt sea was frozen on her breast,
The salt tears in her eyes;
And her streaming hair, like the brown sea-weed,
On the waves did fall and rise.

Such was the wreck of the Hesperus,
In the midnight and the snow!
Oh! save us all from a death like this,
On the reef of 'Norman's Woe'.

Longfellow wrote the poem *The Wreck of the Hesperus* at white heat at midnight on 30 December 1839, in horror at the news of the fate of the schooner *Hesperus* on the reef of Norman's Woe, off Gloucester, Mass. Twenty bodies were delivered by the sea to the beach. One of them was lashed to a spar.

This setting is—let us make no mistake—a masterpiece of its type: the dramatic *scena* popularised by the composer and entertainer Henry Russell. The fact that this piece is unknown to the vast majority of people interested in vocal music shows how far out of perspective we have got the value of nineteenth-century song. If it were only for this one setting, Hatton's name should be known to all musicians. If there are weaknesses they lie in a periodic lapse in word-setting (Longfellow's original takes a little battering in the process) and the accentuation is not always perfect. But the moments of genius outweigh the failings, and a considered performance will melt the hardest heart.

The real Henry Wadsworth Longfellow (1807–1882), suggests *The Reader's Encyclopedia of American Literature*, has to be sought behind 'the steel engraving that once hung in many American school-rooms . . . a serene countenance with a white flowing beard, the patriarch of popular sentiment'. In fact, although the poet knew intense personal grief—his first wife died on a trip to Europe and his second burned to death when curling tongs set fire to her dress—his life was singularly placid and that steel engraving genuinely reflected the geniality and nobility of his visage. Charles Kingsley remarked that Longfellow possessed the most beautiful human face he had ever seen. The truth is that Longfellow did live the image of the patriarch of American poetry, writing facile and sentimental verses that went straight to the hearts of the English-speaking peoples. Even if he lacked profundity and originality he had other attributes in abundance. He could never be less than melodious and composers vied to set his lyrics to music.

A note on John Liptrot Hatton appears on page 26.

Three Fishers Went Sailing

Written by the REV. CHARLES KINGSLEY

Composed by JOHN HULLAH

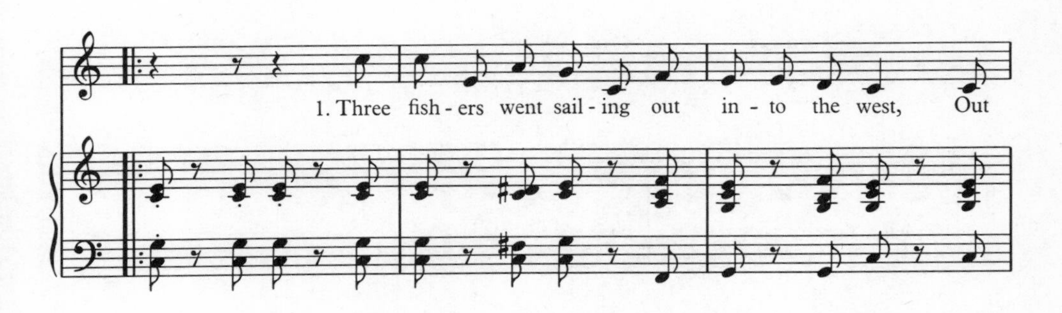

un poco rall.
lov'd him the best, And the child - ren stood watch - ing them
f
a tempo
out of the town; For men must work, and wo-men must weep, And there's
pp
cresc.
lit-tle to earn, and ma-ny to keep, Tho' the har - bour bar be
fz
cresc.
f
moan - - - - - - - ing.
fz
dim.
pp
Last time only
pp
dim.

Three Fishers Went Sailing

1. Three fishers went sailing out into the west,
   Out into the west as the sun went down;
   Each thought on the woman who lov'd him the best,
   And the children stood watching them out of the town;
   For men must work, and women must weep,
   And there's little to earn, and many to keep,
   Tho' the harbour bar be moaning.

2. Three wives sat up in the lighthouse tow'r,
   And they trimm'd the lamps as the sun went down;
   They look'd at the squall, and they look'd at the show'r,
   And the night-rack came rolling up ragged and brown!
   But men must work, and women must weep,
   Though storms be sudden, and waters deep,
   And the harbour bar be moaning.

3. Three corpses lay out on the shining sands
   In the morning gleam as the tide went down,
   And the women are weeping and wringing their hands
   For those who will never come back to the town;
   For men must work, and women must weep,
   And the sooner it's over, the sooner to sleep,
   And goodbye to the bar and its moaning.

Not surprisingly, this song had an instantaneous success when first performed by Madame Antoinette Sterling at a ballad concert: 'there was a tumult of applause; people rose in their places and cheered, waving hats and handkerchiefs in their excitement'. Madame Sterling said afterwards that although she had never been to sea in a storm nor had even seen fishermen, she understood the piece by instinct. She was helped by a very pleasant setting. The gentle *siciliano* rhythm sets the mood, a reflection of the resignation in the words. No one who has heard Clara Butt's famous recording of this song with its low E in bar nine of the vocal line could fail to be moved. The higher E as it appears in this arrangement is perfectly satisfactory and less dangerous. 'Three Fishers' enjoyed great prestige for many years among performers whose technique was not overtaxed by the relatively straightforward vocal line and simple piano part.

The Reverend Charles Kingsley (1819–1875), son of a Devon parson, received his education and love for the manlier outdoor sports and also his introduction to religious doubts at Cambridge. Despite inward conflict he became curate and later rector of Eversley in Hampshire, a living he retained until his death. He taught history at Cambridge, involved himself deeply in Christian Socialism and social reform, and produced all manner of literary work, ranging from songs and poetry to works on natural history. His children's book, *The Water Babies*, has a sententious ring today, but his historical novels such as *Westward Ho!* and *Hereward the Wake* still provide a robust read. His sermons had a fine reputation, too, and when Queen Victoria invited him to preach at Buckingham Palace his earlier socialism seemed to have evaporated.

Dr John Pyke Hullah (1812–1884) is chiefly celebrated as an educator of the English masses in the elements of music. Born at Worcester, he was reputedly of Huguenot descent. He went to the Royal Academy of Music and three years later his opera *The Village Coquettes*, with words by Charles Dickens, was produced. Two more operas failed and Hullah found a fresh vocation in teaching music by a simple system of syllables instead of conventional notation (thought to be beyond the intellect of the poor), devised by Mainzer in Paris and developed by Wilhelm. The time was ripe for an excursion in mass musical instruction: music was seen as an ameliorating force that could divert the lower classes from grosser pursuits. For the rest of his life Hullah devoted himself to the cause, but his career was far from smooth. Unfortunately he had backed the wrong system: the slightly more sophisticated Tonic Sol-Fa method, propagated by John Curwen, took the lead. Hullah also played the organ, conducted, composed church music, lectured, promoted concerts and wrote songs, among them settings in 1858 of 'Three Fishers' and 'The Sands of Dee', poems by his friend Charles Kingsley.

White Wings

Written and composed by BANKS WINTER

Sail home to sweet Mag - gie Dar - row In her
dear lit - tle home she is wait - ing for me.
rit.
rit.
a tempo
High up! where cliffs they are crag - gy,
There's where the girl of my heart waits for me!
Heigh ho I long for you Mag - gie I'll

rall.
spread out my 'White Wings' and sail home to thee Yo! ho, how we
go! Oh! how the winds blow!
CHORUS
f
'White Wings' they ne - ver grow wea - ry, They car - ry me chee - ri - ly
'White Wings' they ne - ver grow wea - ry, They car - ry me chee - ri - ly
'White Wings' they ne - ver grow wea - ry, They car - ry me chee - ri - ly
'White Wings' they ne - ver grow wea - ry, They car - ry me chee - ri - ly

o - ver the sea; Night comes! I long for my dea - ry I'll
o - ver the sea; Night comes! I long for my dea - ry I'll
o - ver the sea; Night comes! I long for my dea - ry
o - ver the sea; Night comes! I long for my dea - ry
rall.
spread out my 'White Wings' and sail home to thee!
rall.
spread out my 'White Wings' and sail home to thee!
to thee!
to thee!
rall.

White Wings

1. Sail! home as straight as an arrow,
   My yacht shoots along on the crest of the sea;
   Sail home to sweet Maggie Darrow
   In her dear little home she is waiting for me.
   High up! where the cliffs are craggy,
   There's where the girl of my heart waits for me!
   Heigh ho I long for you Maggie
   I'll spread out my 'White Wings' and sail home to thee
   Yo! ho, how we go!
   Oh! how the winds blow!

CHORUS: 'White Wings' they never grow weary,
They carry me cheerily over the sea;
Night comes! I long for my deary,
I'll spread out my 'White Wings' and sail home to thee!

2. Sail! home to love and caresses,
   When Maggie my darling is there at my side;
   Sail home blue eyes and gold tresses
   The fairest of all is my own little bride.
   Sail! home to part from thee never,
   Always together life's voyage shall be.
   Sail! home to love thee for ever
   I'll spread out my 'White Wings' and sail home to thee
   Yo! ho, how we go!
   Oh! how the winds blow!

CHORUS: 'White Wings' they never grow weary, etc.

Banks Winter, who hailed from Georgia, was a tenor in leading Minstrel companies. He bought the rights in an unsuccessful song called 'White Wings' by Joseph Gulick which the latter had written in 1882. Banks went right back to the novel of the same name by William Black that had inspired the piece originally, and composed the words and music for a completely new song. Although the melody is immediately appealing the new version did not catch on. No publisher would take it up and no audience respond to its saccharine tones. A baritone, J. P. O'Keefe, a fellow Minstrel in the Thatcher, Primrose and West troupe, planned to include it in the programme in New York, but despite Winter's membership of the company permission to sing it was refused by the management. Fortunately the musical director suggested that a change of key might help: this appears to have made all the difference. The composer was allowed to sing 'White Wings' in Boston in 1884 and it was an immediate hit, its celebrity spreading to the rest of America and to Britain very swiftly. Winter wrote other songs, but none of them repeated the success of 'White Wings'. The actress and singer Winona Winter is said to have been Banks Winter's daughter, but David Ewen's *Popular American Composers* ascribes her parentage to Harry von Tilzer.

Incidentally, Sigmund Spaeth points to the popular misconception that 'White Wings' referred to the coats of New York street cleaners instead of to the sails of a boat.

Anchored

Written by SAMUEL K. COWAN Composed by MICHAEL WATSON

Fly - ing with feath' - ry prow, Bound-ing with slant - ing keel And
glad and glad was the sai - - lor lad, As he
cresc.
sf
p
cresc.
steer'd and sang at his wheel.
f
f
mf
"On - ly an - o - ther day to stray,
mf
On - ly an - o - ther night to roam, Then

f
safe at last, the har - bour past, Safe in my
mf
fa - ther's home, Safe in my
f
poco rit.
fa - ther's home!"
poco rit.
ff a tempo
sf
sf
Moderato
Bright on the flash - ing brine, Glit - ter'd the sum - mer sun!
p staccato

Anchored

Sweet - ly the star - ry shine Smil'd when the day was done!
p
Blithe was the breeze of Heav'n, Fil- ling the fly - ing sail, And
rall.
glad was the sai - lor lad, As he steer'd and sang thro' the
p
mf a tempo
gale. "On - ly an - o - ther day to stray,
f
mf
On - ly an - o - ther night to roam, Then

f
safe at last, the har - bour past, Safe in my
mf
fa - ther's home, Safe in my
f
poco rit.
fa - ther's home!"
poco rit.
ff a tempo
sf
sf
Agitato
Sud-den the light - nings flash'd, Like fal - chions in the
mf

Anchored

cresc.
f
dark! Sud-den the thun - ders crash'd! A -
cresc.
f
molto rall.
Andante
- las! for the gal - lant bark! There when the storm had pass'd, A
sf
p
p
p
drea - ry wreck lay she! But bright was the star - ry light, That
p
rall.
p Allegretto
shone on the sum mer sea! And a soft smile came from the
rall.
pp
3
stars, And a voice from the whisp - 'ring

cresc.
poco
foam.
Safe, safe at last, the
a
poco
dan - ger past,
Safe in his Fa - ther's
f
Home!
Safe in his Fa - ther's
f
Home!
ad lib.
Safe in his
ff colla voce
rall.
Fa - ther's Home!
rall.
ff
sf
sf
sf

Anchored

1. Flying, with flowing sail,
 Over the summer sea!
 Sheer thro' the seething gale,
 Homeward bound was she!
 Flying with feath'ry prow,
 Bounding with slanting keel
 And glad was the sailor lad,
 As he steer'd and sang at his wheel.

CHORUS: 'Only another day to stray,
Only another night to roam,
Then safe at last, the harbour past,
Safe in my father's home!'

2. Bright on the flashing brine,
 Glitter'd the summer sun!
 Sweetly the starry shine
 Smil'd when the day was done!
 Blithe was the breeze of heav'n,
 Filling the flying sail,
 And glad was the sailor lad
 As he steer'd and sang thro' the gale.

CHORUS: 'Only another day to stray, etc.

3. Sudden the lightnings flash'd,
 Like falchions in the dark!
 Sudden the thunders crash'd!
 Alas! for the gallant bark!
 There when the storm had pass'd,
 A dreary wreck lay she!
 But bright was the starry light,
 That shone on the summer sea!

4. And a soft smile came from the stars,
 And a voice from the whisp'ring foam.
 Safe, safe at last, the danger past,
 Safe in his Father's Home!

On the front of the sheet music the publisher (the composer John Blockley) proclaimed that 'Anchored' realised £1212.15.0, 'the largest price, we believe, that has ever been given for a song', and quoted *The Times* as authority. It is interesting to see that at a time when a song could be available in a multiplicity of keys for a variety of voices, 'Anchored' was published in no less than twenty-five versions including three duets, two trios, several piano solos, as a waltz, as a march, and in a setting for cornet à piston. The legend 'Anchored (in G)' which was appended to the foot of each page of the sheet music was not intended to mislead the singer as to the harmonic language of this fine bravura piece!

Although a conventional ballad in many ways—indeed it is rather a mini-*scena* of the Henry Russell type—it has enough fine and stirring music to assure it a place among the finest songs of the period. Neither do the *religioso* implications of the text go unnoticed in this setting: quasi-recitative greets the calm after the storm and *tremolando* writing reinforces the safe arrival in heaven of the Sailor Lad. The way the poet alters a human father for the Eternal Father in the last verse is rather neat, too.

Samuel Kennedy Cowan (not to be confused with the composer Sir Frederic Cowen) was a prolific though minor English poet whose published work includes *Idylls of Ireland, The Murmur of the Shells, The Pet Swan and Other Poems* and *Verses in Commemoration of the Coming of Age of the Marquis of Devonshire.*

William Michael Watson (1840–1889) was an English vocal and instrumental composer, born in Newcastle-upon-Tyne. He had a particularly effective line in sea songs.

Asleep in the Deep

Written by ARTHUR J. LAMB

Composed by H. W. PETRIE

f

ff

f

1. Storm-y the night and the waves roll high, Brave-ly the ship doth ride,

mf

Hark! while the light-house bell's sol - emn cry
Rings o'er the sul - len tide.
cresc.
There on the deck see two lov - ers stand,
Heart to heart beat-ing, and hand to hand; Tho'
mf
death be near, she knows no fear
While at her side is one of all most dear.
cresc.
REFRAIN
Loud - ly the bell in the old tow-er rings,
mf
Bid - ding us list to the warn - ing it brings:

Sail - or, take care!
Sail - or, take care!
ff
Dan - ger is near thee, Be - ware! Be - ware!
Be - - - ware! Be - - - ware!
p
ad lib.
Ma-ny brave hearts are a-sleep in the deep, So be-ware! be - ware!
cresc.
Ma - ny brave hearts are a-sleep in the deep, So be-ware! be - ware!
p

Asleep in the Deep

1. Stormy the night and the waves roll high,
   Bravely the ship doth ride,
   Hark! while the lighthouse bell's solemn cry
   Rings o'er the sullen tide.
   There on the deck see two lovers stand,
   Heart to heart beating, and hand to hand;
   Tho' death be near, she knows no fear
   While at her side is one of all most dear.

CHORUS: Loudly the bell in the old tower rings,
Bidding us list to the warning it brings:—
Sailor, take care! Sailor, take care!
Danger is near thee, beware! beware!
Many brave hearts are asleep in the deep, so beware! beware!

2. What of the storm when the night is o'er?
   There is no trace or sign.
   Save where the wreckage hath strewn the shore,
   Peaceful the sun doth shine.
   But when the wild, raging storm did cease,
   Under the billows two hearts found peace,
   No more to part, no more of pain,
   The bell may now tell its warning in vain.

CHORUS: Loudly the bell in the old tower rings, etc.

Here is another song for the nautically-minded basso profundo. The vocal gymnastics required of the singer at the end of the refrain should not deter the amateur possessed of an ordinary vocal range from revelling in this charming if slight ballad.

Arthur J. Lamb (1870–1928) was a Minstrel who came from England. He was a prolific Tin Pan Alley lyricist, in full spate from the 'nineties until the First World War. He returned to the nautical vein with the somewhat gloomy 'When the Bell in the Lighthouse Rings Ding Dong', and provided words for more frivolous pieces like 'The Bird on Nellie's Hat' and 'You'll Splash Me and I'll Splash You'. His one great hit was 'Only a Bird in a Gilded Cage' for which Harry von Tilzer composed the music. Arthur Lamb should not be confused with Henry Lamb who wrote 'The Volunteer Organist', on page 153.

Henry W. Petrie (1857–1925) composed 'Asleep in the Deep' in 1897. He was a black-face Minstrel, and wrote quite a number of ballads around the turn of the century but only one other is still sung today, the famous 'tot' song 'I Don't Want to Play in Your Yard' with lyric by Philip Wingate.

The Sympathetic Tear

The Arab's Farewell to his Steed

Written by the HON. MRS NORTON

Composed by JOHN BLOCKLEY

eye; Fret not to roam the de - sert now, With
all thy wing - ed speed; I may not mount on
mf
thee a - gain, Thou'rt sold, my_ A - rab steed! Fret not with that im -
mf
- pa - tient hoof, Snuff not the breez - y wind: The fur - ther that thou
cresc.
fli - est now, So far am I be - hind. The stran - ger hath thy
p

bri - dle rein— Thy mas-ter hath his gold— Fleet limb'd and beau-ti-ful,
fare thee well! Thou'rt sold, my steed, thou'rt sold!
dim. e rall.
f
mf a tempo
dim.
f
2. The morn - ing sun shall dawn a-gain, But nev-er more with
p
thee Shall I gal-lop thro' the des-ert paths, Where
mf

we were wont to be: Ev'n-ing shall dark-en
mf
on the earth, and o'er the san-dy plain, Some
rall.
o-ther steed, with slow-er step, Shall bear me_home a-gain.
When the dim dis-tance cheats mine eye, And thro' the ga-th'ring
p
tears Thy bright form for a mo-ment, like The false mi-rage ap-

-pears, Then sit-ting down by that green well, I'll pause and sad - ly
pp
colla voce
molto rall.
think, "'Twas here he_bow'd his glos-sy neck When last I saw him drink."
colla voce
Agitato e accellerando
3. When last I saw thee drink!— a-way! The fe-ver'd dream is
mf
f
o'er,— I could not live a day, and know That we should meet no
ff
more. They tempt-ed me, my beau-ti - ful! For hun - ger's pow'r is
Tempo
ff
mf

strong, They tempt - ed me, my beau - ti - ful, But
f
cresc.
I have lov'd too long.
risoluto
Who said that I had
3
giv'n thee up? Who said that thou wert sold? 'Tis
appassionato
false, 'tis false, my Ar - ab steed, I fling them back their
sf

animato
gold! Thus, *thus,* I leap up – on thy back, And
scour the dis – tant plains; A – way, who o – ver –
– takes us now, Shall claim *thee* for his pains.
f
f
sf
ff

The Arab's Farewell to his Steed

1. My beautiful, my beautiful,
   That standest meekly by,
With thy proudly arch'd and glossy neck,
   And dark and fiery eye;
Fret not to roam the desert now,
   With all thy wingèd speed;
I may not mount on thee again,
   Thou'rt sold, my Arab steed.

Fret not with that impatient hoof,
   Snuff not the breezy wind:
The farther that thou fliest now
   So far am I behind.
The stranger hath thy bridle rein—
   Thy master hath his gold—
Fleet limb'd and beautiful, fare thee well!
   Thou'rt sold, my steed, thou'rt sold!

2. The morning sun shall dawn again,
   But never more with thee,
Shall I gallop thro' the desert paths,
   Where we were wont to be.
Ev'ning shall darken on the earth,
   And o'er the sandy plain,
Some other steed, with slower step,
   Shall bear me home again.
When the dim distance cheats mine eye
   And thro' the gath'ring tears
Thy bright form for a moment, like
   The false mirage appears,
Then sitting down by that green well,
   I'll pause and sadly think,
' 'Twas *here* he bow'd his glossy neck
   When last I saw him drink.'

3. *When last I saw thee drink!*—away!
   The fever'd dream is o'er,
I could not live a day, and *know*
   That we should meet no more.
They tempted me, my beautiful!
   For hunger's pow'r is strong,
They tempted me, my beautiful!
   But I have lov'd too long.
Who said that I had giv'n thee up?
   Who said that thou wert sold?
'Tis false, 'tis false, my Arab steed,
   I fling them back their gold!
Thus, *thus* I leap upon thy back,
   And scour the distant plains;
Away, who overtakes us now,
   Shall claim *thee* for his pains.

The Hon. Mrs Norton (see page 30 for biographical details) here makes a notable excursion into the Victorian fantasy land of the Orient, an amalgam of the desert, the near and middle East, and the fairy-tale trappings of *The Arabian Nights Entertainments.* The first lines of the song were wont to be applied to high-mettled Victorian ladies by their gentlemen admirers. The text printed here truncates Mrs Norton's poem and uses what is left in fairly casual fashion. This version is a conflation of two editions, and the punctuation and italicisation have been tidied from the somewhat exuberant originals. Blockley's setting has one or two nice touches: notice the Arab's agony portrayed by means of the minor third of 'Thou'rt sold, my Arab steed', and also the rolling desert and galloping hooves in the accompaniment.

John Blockley (1801–1882) was one of the most indefatigable and prolific composers of the nineteenth, or indeed any other century. This tireless Englishman set to music the verse of practically all the admired poets of the time. Scarcely a line of Tennyson escaped him; Longfellow's ink was hardly dry before Blockley was at work; and he scurried to set innumerable effusions by Mrs Hemans, the Hon. Mrs Norton, Eliza Cook, Bishop Heber and Martin Farquhar Tupper. He kept three publishers busy and turned music publisher himself. It is sad therefore to have to report that despite this prodigious labour very few of his songs are really worth revival.

Listen to the Mocking Bird

Written and composed by ALICE HAWTHORNE (SEPTIMUS WINNER)

Hal - ly, I'm dream - ing now of Hal - ly, For the
thought of her is one that ne - ver dies;
She's sleep - ing in the
val - ley, the val - ley, the val - ley, She's sleep - ing in the
val - ley, And the mock - ing bird is sing - ing where she lies.
CHORUS
List - en to the mock - ing bird, List - en to the

mock-ing bird, The mock-ing bird still sing-ing o'er her
grave; List-en to the mock-ing bird, List-en to the
mock-ing bird, Still sing-ing where the weep ing wil-lows wave.
QUARTETTE
List-en to the mock-ing bird, List-en to the
List-en to the mock-ing bird, List-en to the
List-en to the mock-ing bird, List-en to the
List-en to the mock-ing bird, List-en to the
8va
tr
tr

mock-ing bird, The mock-ing bird still sing-ing o'er her
mock-ing bird, The mock-ing bird still sing-ing o'er her
mock-ing bird, The mock-ing bird still sing-ing o'er her
mock-ing bird The mock-ing bird still sing-ing o'er her
8va
tr
grave; List-en to the mock-ing bird, List-en to the
grave; List-en to the mock-ing bird, List-en to the
grave; List-en to the mock-ing bird, List-en to the
grave; List-en to the mock-ing bird, List-en to the
8va
tr

mock-ing bird, Still sing-ing where the weep-ing wil-lows wave.
mock-ing bird, Still sing-ing where the weep-ing wil-lows wave.
mock-ing bird, Still sing-ing where the weep-ing wil-lows wave.
mock-ing bird, Still sing-ing where the weep-ing wil-lows wave.
8va
tr
8va
tr
8va
tr

Listen to the Mocking Bird

1. I'm dreaming now of Hally, sweet Hally, sweet Hally,
For the thought of her is one that never dies;
She's sleeping in the valley, the valley, the valley,
And the mocking bird is singing where she lies.

CHORUS: Listen to the mocking bird,
Listen to the mocking bird,
The mocking bird still singing o'er her grave;
Listen to the mocking bird,
Listen to the mocking bird,
Still singing where the weeping willows wave.

2. Ah! well I yet remember, remember, remember,
When we gather'd in the cotton side by side;
'Twas in the mild September, September, September,
And the mocking bird was singing far and wide.

CHORUS: Listen to the mocking bird, etc.

3. When the charms of spring awaken, awaken, awaken,
And the mocking bird is singing on the bough,
I feel like one forsaken, forsaken, forsaken,
Since my Hally is no longer with me now.

CHORUS: Listen to the mocking bird, etc.

The warbling refrain was originally the inspiration of a Philadelphia Negro barber, Dick Milburn, who also begged for his bread. The composer whose name is usually given to the melody overheard Milburn's imitation of the mocking bird, appropriated it and elaborated it into this song (published in 1855 as a 'Sentimental Ethiopian Ballad') which has been much appreciated down the years by whistlers who enjoy imitating bird calls. Nevertheless, this is a song well worth revival for its musical qualities alone. It exhibits a superbly managed string of sequences and the imitation of the mocking bird in the piano part of the chorus cannot fail to bring a smile to the dourest face. The cheerfulness of the setting relieves the gloom of the words. Abraham Lincoln is said to have declared the song like the 'laughter of a little girl at play'.

'Alice Hawthorne' was really Septimus Winner (1826 or 7–1902) who chose his mother's maiden name as one of his pseudonyms. Another well-known song of his, 'Come Where the Woodbine Twineth', appeared under the name of Apsley Street. Born at Philadelphia, Winner studied the violin and opened a music store in his home town, giving music lessons on fiddle, guitar and banjo. He wrote for *Graham's Magazine*, and produced tutors for musical instruments, among them a banjo primer. He became a music publisher, too, forming the company of Winner & Shuster. Winner is credited with over two thousand compositions, the bulk of them songs including the touching 'What is Home Without a Mother?', and he was responsible for the words of 'Oh Where, Oh Where Has My Little Dog Gone'. Once his song-writing got him into trouble: a piece advocating the return of General McClellan reflected popular sentiment but infuriated the authorities. It landed him in jail for a time, the only composer known to have been tried for treason.

In the Gloaming

Written by META ORRED Composed by ANNIE FORTESCUE HARRISON

Agitato
When the winds are sob - bing faint - ly, with a gen - tle
For my heart was crush'd with long - ing, what had been could
con anima
un - known woe, Will you think of me, and love me,
nev - er be. It was best to leave you thus, dear,
1
2
rall.
as you did once long a - go?
best for you and best for me; It was
cresc.
cresc.
best to leave you thus; ... Best for you and best for me....
colla voce

In the Gloaming

1. In the gloaming, oh, my darling, when the lights are dim and low;
   And the quiet shadows falling, softly come and softly go;
   When the winds are sobbing faintly, with a gentle unknown woe,
   Will you think of me, and love me, as you did once long ago?

2. In the gloaming, oh, my darling, think not bitterly of me!
   Though I pass'd away in silence, left you lonely, set you free,
   For my heart was crush'd with longing, what had been could never be.
   It was best to leave you thus, dear, best for you and best for me.

Composed in the late 'seventies (the American publication was 1877), 'In the Gloaming' gained immense currency despite its quiet, unpretentious character. It is a beautiful little song with an intangible, sweet melancholy for the 'gentle unknown woe'. As Willson Disher says: it 'distils the sweetness of years when the family was our whole world'.

Annie Fortescue Harrison (1851–1944) was also known as a song-writer under her married name, Lady Arthur Hill. She composed in similar vein 'Let Me Forget Thee' and 'The Waning Years'. Her husband had the august post of Comptroller of the Household of Her Majesty Queen Victoria.

Despite her curious name which looks very like an anagram, Meta Orred really did exist. She was a poetess whose work was published in the 'seventies, and she lived on until 1953. 'In the Gloaming' first appeared in a collection of her poems in 1874.

Daddy

Written by MARY MARK LEMON

Composed by ARTHUR BEHREND

Moderato

mf

1. Take my head on your shoul - der, Dad - dy Turn your face to the

west, It is just the hour when the sky turns gold, The

hour___ that mo - ther loves best. The day has been long with -

poco accel.

poco accel.

out you, Dad-dy, You've been such a-while a - way And
now you're as tir'd of your work, Dad-dy, As I am tir'd of my
a tempo
play; But I've got you And you've got me, So ev'-ry-thing seems
a tempo
rall.
right. I won-der if mo-ther is think-ing of us, Be-
rall.
rit.
a tempo
-cause it is my birth - day night!
rit.
a tempo

2. Why do your big tears fall, Dad-dy?
Mo-ther's not far a - way,
I of - ten seem to hear her voice
Fal-ling a - cross my play,
poco accel.
And it some-times makes me cry, Dad-dy, To
poco accel.
think it's none of it true,
Till I fall a - sleep, to dream, Dad-dy, Of
home, and mo-ther and you.
For I've got you, and you've got me, So

rall.
ev - 'ry thing may go, We're all the world to each o-ther, Dad-dy, For
rall.
colla voce
rit.
a tempo
mo-ther, dear mo-ther once told me so.
3. I'm
rit.
a tempo
sometimes a - fraid to think, Dad-dy, When I am big like you, And
you are old and grey, Dad-dy, What you and I would do, If,
when we got up to Hea - ven, And mo-ther was wait - ing there, She

should-n't re-mem-ber the two she left, So sad and so lone-ly
here But year by year, still sees no change, And so 'twill all be
right, We shall al-ways meet her in our dreams, Daddy, good night,
ad lib.
Dad-dy, good night, dear Dad-dy, dear Dad-dy, good night, good
night.

Daddy

1. Take my head on your shoulder, Daddy,
   Turn your face to the west,
It is just the hour when the sky turns gold,
   The hour that mother loves best.
The day has been long without you, Daddy,
   You've been such a while away—
And now you're as tir'd of your work, Daddy,
   As I am tir'd of my play;
But I've got you and you've got me,
   So ev'rything seems right—
I wonder if mother is thinking of us,
   Because it is my birthday night!

2. Why do your big tears fall, Daddy?
   Mother's not far away,
I often seem to hear her voice
   Falling across my play,
And it sometimes makes me cry, Daddy,
   To think it's none of it true,
Till I fall asleep, to dream, Daddy,
   Of home, and mother and you—
For I've got you, and you've got me,
   So ev'rything may go,
We're all the world to each other, Daddy,
   For mother, dear mother once told me so.

3. I'm sometimes afraid to think, Daddy,
   When I am big like you,
And you are old and grey, Daddy,
   What you and I would do,
If, when we got up to Heaven,
   And mother was waiting there,
She shouldn't remember the two she left,
   So sad and so lonely here.
But year by year, still sees no change,
   And so 'twill all be right,
We shall always meet her in our dreams,
   Dear Daddy, dear Daddy, good night.

'Daddy' was made especially famous by Dame Clara Butt whose contralto rendering moistened many an eye. It is a companion piece to Behrend's 'Auntie' (which is included in *The Parlour Song Book*) and there was another song called 'Mother', too. For many people 'Daddy' represents the archetypal Victorian ballad, largely because of its subject matter. A closer look at the song itself will identify other aspects. Behrend manages to build up an atmosphere of childish simplicity contrasted with adult complexity. From the lullaby rhythms of the opening through the agitato 'I'm sometimes afraid to think, Daddy . . .' to the assured stability of the cadence he follows the changing mood of the child. The bouncy rhythm and tune of 'For I've got you, and you've got me' appears at regular intervals and wrenches the song from its reverie, mirroring the butterfly mind of the child who has assimilated the catch-phrases of adults without really understanding them. It is such delicate brush-strokes as these that make this piece worthy of closer inspection and of a more considered judgement than one might give a routine sentimental ballad.

Mary Mark Lemon, whose other songs include 'The Old Cathedral' with music by Ciro Pinsuti, was possibly one of the seven daughters of Mark Lemon (1809–1870), prolific dramatist and co-founder and first editor of *Punch*.

Arthur Henry Behrend (1853–1935), born in Danzig, came on his father's side of a noble Swedish family and on his mother's from the Irish composer M. W. Balfe, whence no doubt descended his melodic gift. Educated at the English public school Haileybury, Behrend started his career in commerce. He threw this up after a year to study music, and became one of England's most tuneful song-writers, composing over two hundred ballads as well as cantatas and unpublished operas.

On the Banks of the Wabash, Far Away

Written and Composed by PAUL DRESSER

first re-ceived my les-sons — Na-ture's school, But
one thing there is miss-ing in the pic - ture, With-
rall.
out her face it seems so in-com - plete, I
rall.
long to see my moth-er in the door - way, As she
a tempo
rall.
p
stood there years a - go, her boy to greet.
rall.
p

On the Banks of the Wabash, Far Away

On the Banks of the Wabash, Far Away

1. Round my Indiana homestead wave the corn-fields,
   In the distance loom the woodlands clear and cool,
Often times my tho'ts revert to scenes of childhood,
   Where I first received my lessons—Nature's school.
But one thing there is missing in the picture,
   Without her face it seems so incomplete,
I long to see my mother in the doorway,
   As she stood there years ago, her boy to greet.

CHORUS: Oh, the moonlight's fair tonight along the Wabash,
From the fields there comes the breath of new-mown hay,
Through the sycamores the candle lights are gleaming,
On the banks of the Wabash, far away.

2. Many years have passed since I strolled by the river,
   Arm in arm, with sweetheart Mary by my side,
It was there I tried to tell her that I loved her,
   It was there I begged of her to be my bride.
Long years have passed since I strolled thro' the churchyard,
   She's sleeping there my angel Mary dear,
I loved her but she thought I didn't mean it,
   Still I'd give my future were she only here.

CHORUS: Oh, the moonlight's fair tonight along the Wabash, etc.

This lovely song of 1891 can only be a product of the American genius. Although written to a formula, it has the sweep of unforced melody from a relatively unsophisticated composer that places it on the same level as the best of Stephen Foster. It follows the Tin Pan Alley blueprint very closely. The verse is expressed in two-bar phrases making four-bar sentences, A, A, B, A, where B is—as so often—in the relative minor and where other modulations are kept to closely related keys. The chorus divides into two-bar phrases, A, B, A, C. Notwithstanding the frequency of its use, the formula seldom palls, and in Dresser's song it provides the vehicle for one of the happiest pieces of composition in this book. The dotted crotchet, quaver figure in the chorus gives the lazy feeling of a slow blues and the cadential clichés add the finishing touches.

There is some disagreement about the provenance of the song. One school claims that Paul Dresser's novelist brother Theodore Dreiser roughed it out for him, and a rival party supports the claim of the composer and conductor Max Hoffman to have helped in Dresser's struggles to get the song down on paper, slaving over a hot reed organ in a Chicago hotel room to do so. Be either story as it may, there is no doubt that the piece belongs essentially to Dresser, and is completely in accord stylistically with his other compositions.

Paul Dresser (1857–1906) was born Paul Dreiser at Terre Haute, Indiana, on the banks of the Wabash. His brother, Theodore, became a famous novelist. Their deeply religious father wanted Paul to be a priest but the boy loved music too much. He ran away from home and joined a medicine show, soon to write songs and join the Billy Rice

Minstrels as an end-man. His compositions brought him large sums which were dissipated in high living, extravagant even among the extravagances of Tin Pan Alley. In 1901 he went into partnership with his publisher and two years later the firm failed. Now wretched and deserted by his fair-weather friends, he died, it is said, of a broken heart. Ironically, his last song, 'My Gal Sal', was published too late for him to profit from its success. Another piece of his, the pathetic 'The Pardon Came Too Late', appears in *The Parlour Song Book.*

Poor But Honest

The Old Arm Chair

Written by ELIZA COOK

Composed by HENRY RUSSELL

-dew'd it with tears, and em-balm'd it with sighs; 'Tis bound by a thou - sand
bands to my heart; Not a tie will break, not a link will start. Would ye
learn the spell, a moth-er sat there, And a sa - cred thing is that
f
f
p
old arm chair.
cresc.
2. I sat and watch'd her
ma - ny a day When her eye grew dim, and her locks were grey; And I

al-most worshipp'd her when she smil'd, And turn'd from her bi-ble to
bless her child, Years roll'd on, but the last one sped, My
i-dol was shatter'd, my earth-star fled: I learnt how much the
heart can bear, When I saw her die in that old arm chair.
3. 'Tis past! 'tis past! but I gaze on it now With

qui-ver - ing breath and throb - bing brow; 'Twas there she nursed me, 'twas
there she died; And mem' - ry flows with la - va tide,
Say it is fol-ly, and deem me weak, While the scald - ing drops start
down my cheek; But I love it, I love it, and can - not tear My
rall.
soul from a mo-ther's old arm chair.
p
cresc.
p

The Old Arm Chair

1. I love it, I love it, and who shall dare
   To chide me for loving that old arm chair,
   I've treasured it long as a holy prize,
   I've bedew'd it with tears, and embalm'd it with sighs;
   'Tis bound by a thousand bands to my heart;
   Not a tie will break it, not a link will start.
   Would ye learn the spell, a mother sat there,
   And a sacred thing is that old arm chair.

2. I sat and watch'd her many a day
   When her eye grew dim, and her locks were grey;
   And I almost worshipp'd her when she smil'd,
   And turn'd from her bible to bless her child,
   Years roll'd on, but the last one sped,
   My idol was shatter'd, my earth-star fled;
   I learnt how much the heart can bear,
   When I saw her die in that old arm chair.

3. 'Tis past! 'tis past! but I gaze on it now
   With quivering breath and throbbing brow;
   'Twas there she nursed me, 'twas there she died;
   And mem'ry flows with lava tide,
   Say it is folly, and deem me weak,
   While the scalding drops start down my cheek;
   But I love it, I love it, and cannot tear
   My soul from a mother's old arm chair.

Written by Eliza Cook in 1836, a year before Queen Victoria ascended to the throne, and composed by Henry Russell a couple of years later, this ballad started a number of fashions that flowered greatly during our period. 'The Old Arm Chair' is an early example of the genre of song that used domestic furniture to trigger off nostalgic family recollections. The word 'old' was to prove an infallible ingredient in such ballads. The century long it dominated the lists of titles: old arm chairs, oaks, spinning wheels, clocks, rustic bridges, dogs, soldiers, sailors, sextons and rugged crosses. Russell squeezed all he could out of the device: one of his songs, 'The Drunkard', begins with 'The old lamp burned on the old oaken stool'. Stephen Foster was to catch the virus badly and gave vent to 'Old Uncle Ned', 'Old Folks at Home', 'My Old Kentucky Home', 'Old Dog Tray', 'Old Memories' and 'Old Black Joe'. Not only was this song one of the youngest of the olds, it also started the vogue for mammy ballads, a genre that was adopted enthusiastically by the black-face Minstrels.

Eliza Cook (1818–1889), poetess, was the youngest of the eleven children of a London brasier. She exhibited literary tendencies at an early age and some of her most celebrated poems appeared in *Lays of a Wild Harp* published when she was but seventeen. She contributed to newspapers for many years, and in 1849 launched her own periodical, the mild and moral *Eliza Cook's Journal* which survived only five years. In later life she was dogged by bad health and her powers began to fail. A grateful government, however, recognised her long service to the middle-class muse with an annual pension of a hundred pounds.

The Old Arm Chair

Henry Russell (1812–1900) was of Jewish origin and was born at Sheerness on the estuary of the River Thames. His career opened as a boy vocalist and he went to be trained in Italy where he studied under Bellini and met Rossini and Donizetti. Subsequent attempts to live by music in England failed, so young Russell set out for Canada which he found inimical to cultural pursuits. He moved to Rochester, N.Y., where he had a position as organist of the First Presbyterian Church, and started to compose songs, including 'The Old Arm Chair' and 'Woodman, Spare That Tree' (included in *The Parlour Song Book*) as well as such dramatic musical *scenas* as 'The Maniac' and 'The Ship on Fire'. Some success as a member of a group of singers encouraged him to sally forth as a solo entertainer, and he was to earn far more from his songs at the piano than he did from his musical compositions. A stout, whiskery man with dark, curly hair, he overcame an unprepossessing appearance by the brilliance of his performances. His songs tended to reflect his own vocal capabilities; John Hill Hewitt, the American composer, observed that Russell's pieces were designed to make the most of a limited vocal range: 'His "Old Arm Chair", for instance, has but five notes in its melodic construction' (the present editors, by the way, advise a recount). Later Russell took up various social causes, and his songs then did duty to campaign against slavery and to promote temperance. Returning to England in 1841 he continued to perform until retirement in 1865. Even though his last sixty years were spent in England, he is generally regarded as an American composer. One of his sons was the celebrated musician Sir Landon Ronald, who dropped his surname of Russell.

The Village Blacksmith

Written by HENRY WADSWORTH LONGFELLOW   Composed by W. H. WEISS

black, and long, His face is like the tan; His brow is wet with
hon - est sweat, He earns what - e'er he can, And looks the whole world
rall.
rall.
in the face For he owes not a - ny man.
Tempo
ff
2. Week in, week out, from morn till night, You can
fz
mf
hear his bel-lows blow; You can hear him swing his hea - vy sledge With
fz

mea - sured beat and slow, Like a sex - ton ring-ing the vil - lage bell, When the
rall.
a tempo
p
even - ing sun is low. And child - ren com-ing home from school Look
f Tempo p
staccato
rall.
a tempo
in at the o - pen door; They love to see the flam - ing forge, And
fz Tempo
mf
hear the bel - lows roar, And catch the burn - ing sparks that fly Like
f
chaff from a thresh-ing floor.
fz
fz
f

3. He goes on Sun - day to the Church, And sits a-mong his
boys; He hears the par - son pray and preach, He hears his daugh-ter's
Old Hundredth Psalm
voice Sing-ing in the vil - lage choir, And it makes his heart re -
- joice: It sounds to him like her mo-ther's voice Sing - ing in Pa - ra -
- dise! He needs must think of her once more, How in the grave she

rall.
lies; And with his hard, rough hand he wipes A tear out of his
pp colla voce
f a tempo
eyes. Toil - ing, re-joic - ing, sor - row-ing, On - ward thro' life he
goes; Each morn - ing sees some task be-gin, Each even - ing sees it
rall.
close; Some thing at-temp-ted, some-thing done, Has earn'd a night's re-
colla voce
- pose.
Tempo f ff

The Village Blacksmith

1. Under a spreading chestnut tree
   The village smithy stands;
The smith, a mighty man is he,
   With large and sinewy hands;
And the muscles of his brawny arms
   Are strong as iron bands.
His hair is crisp, and black, and long,
   His face is like the tan;
His brow is wet with honest sweat,
   He earns whate'er he can,
And looks the whole world in the face
   For he owes not any man.

2. Week in, week out, from morn till night,
   You can hear his bellows blow;
You can hear him swing his heavy sledge
   With measured beat and slow,
Like a sexton ringing the village bell,
   When the evening sun is low.
And children coming home from school
   Look in at the open door;
They love to see the flaming forge,
   And hear the bellows roar,
And catch the burning sparks that fly
   Like chaff from a threshing floor.

3. He goes on Sunday to the Church,
   And sits among his boys;
He hears the parson pray and preach,
   He hears his daughter's voice
Singing in the village choir,
   And it makes his heart rejoice:—
It sounds to him like her mother's voice
   Singing in Paradise!
He needs must think of her once more,
   How in the grave she lies;
And with his hard, rough hand he wipes
   A tear out of his eyes.

Toiling, rejoicing, sorrowing,
   Onward thro' life he goes;
Each morning sees some task begin,
   Each evening sees it close;
Something attempted, something done,
   Has earn'd a night's repose.

'The Village Blacksmith' smote the anvil to the rhythms of several composers, but this setting by Weiss emerged as the most popular. Its standing was such that a perfect crib of the song appeared under the name of B. van de Mortel, copying all Weiss's techniques from the basic rhythms, harmonic movement and accompanimental figures to the snatch of the Old Hundred. That this imitation could exist alongside the original indicates just how ineffective Victorian copyright law was.

The Weiss setting is a good one. Fine muscular lines alternate with subtle touches: the sexton's bell is heard, as is the first half of the Old Hundred hymn tune, and it appears that the blacksmith's wife has been getting on well with her harp practice in heaven. The overall impression, however, is of a simple, sturdy piece completely in style with the subject of the poem.

This is the first of two songs in this book to employ the Old Hundred. The other, 'The Volunteer Organist', is on page 153. The Old Hundredth, as the Americans have it, has an especial place in the American folk consciousness; it is to be found in the famous book of psalms the Pilgrim Fathers carried with them to the new land. Named after the hundredth psalm ('Make a joyful noise unto the Lord, all ye lands . . .'), it has a tune dating from the sixteenth century or even earlier. It has been used for other psalms too, is the tune to which the Doxology is sung ('Praise God from whom all blessings flow') and is perhaps best known as the setting for 'All people that on earth do dwell . . .'

Willoughby Hunter Weiss (1820–1867), the English operatic bass, was the son of a Liverpool professor of the flute and music publisher. He studied under Sir George Smart and M. W. Balfe and excelled on the concert platform, especially in oratorio to which his rich tones were particularly suited. He composed many songs, but only 'The Village Blacksmith' which he set to music in 1854 is remembered now. He originally offered the song to a music publisher for six pounds, but on being turned down published it himself, thus providing himself and his descendants with a comfortable income for the next half-century.

A note on Henry Wadsworth Longfellow appears on page 69.

Close the Shutters, Willie's Dead

Written and composed by JAMES E. STEWART

rall.
Like a dream his spi - rit fled From our home now sad and
drear; When the Springtime flow'rs were bloom - ing,
f
p
And the hap - py birds sang sweet, An - gels call'd him
rall.
to their home, Up in heav'n, where we shall meet.

CHORUS
mf
Close the shut-ters, Wil-lie's gone; Hope with him has fled.
p
rit.
From our home now sad and lone— Close the shut-ters, Wil-lie's dead.
f

Close the Shutters, Willie's Dead

1. Close the shutters, Willie's dead,
   Whom we lov'd so dear.
   Like a dream his spirit fled
   From our home, now sad and drear.
   When the Spring-time flow'rs were blooming,
   And the happy birds sang sweet,
   Angels call'd him to their home,
   Up in heav'n where we shall meet.

CHORUS: Close the shutters, Willie's gone,
Hope with him has fled
From our home, now sad and lone—
Close the shutters, Willie's dead.

2. Close the shutters, Willie's dead,
   Gone in childhood's bloom.
   Pillow'd now his little head
   In the cold and silent tomb.
   O'er his grave the daisies blossom,
   Where his little form is laid
   And the murm'ring streamlet plays,
   'Neath the willow's quiet shade.

CHORUS: Close the shutters, Willie's gone, etc.

3. Close the shutters, Willie's dead,
   Death has claim'd him now.
   Never more his smile will shed
   Sunshine on poor mother's brow.
   She is almost broken-hearted,
   And our home is sad today.
   Life has lost its hope and joy,
   Since our Willie's gone away.

CHORUS: Close the shutters, Willie's gone, etc.

A Minstrel ballad, this exhibits to the full the delight in funeral subject and lachrymose treatment so characteristic of parlour balladry in the 'fifties and 'sixties. Although the verses conform to Voltaire's dictum 'The words that are sung are those which are not fit to be spoken,' and the setting is unexceptional in a style that owes something to Sankey and Moody, this song had a curiously wide celebrity, perhaps because of the graphic title.

James E. Stewart seems to have had a taste for the maudlin; one of his other successes was the pathetic 'Give My Love to All at Home'.

The Beggar Maid

Written by ALFRED, LORD TENNYSON   Composed by SIR JOSEPH BARNBY

rit.
a tempo
king stept down, To meet and greet her on her way; 'It is no
rit.
a tempo
sf
cresc.
won – der,' said the lords, 'it is no won – der,' said the
cresc.
rit.
f
dim. e rall.
lords, 'She is more beau – ti-ful than day, she is more
sf
rit.
dim. e rall.
p
Lento
p
beau – ti – ful than day.' 2. As shines the moon in
p
pp
Tempo Imo
cloud – ed skies, She in her poor at-tire was seen: One prais'd her
sf

cresc.
an - kles, one her eyes, One her dark hair and love-some
cresc.
dim.
p espress.
mien, and love some mien, So sweet a face, such an-gel
pp
grace, In all that land had nev - er been:
f
Co-phe-tua swore a roy - al oath: 'This beg-gar maid
f
ff
shall be my queen, my queen.'
dim.
p
pp

The Beggar Maid

1. Her arms across her breast she laid;
   She was more fair than words can say:
   Barefooted came the beggar maid
   Before the king Cophetua.
   In robe and crown the king stept down,
   To meet and greet her on her way;
   'It is no wonder,' said the lords,
   'She is more beautiful than day.'

2. As shines the moon in clouded skies,
   She in her poor attire was seen:
   One praised her ankles, one her eyes,
   One her dark hair and lovesome mien.
   So sweet a face, such angel grace,
   In all that land had never been:
   Cophetua swore a royal oath:
   'This beggar maid shall be my queen, my queen.'

In 1880 the publisher C. Kegan Paul asked Sir William George Cusins, Master of the Queen's Musick, to edit a collection of songs based on the poetry of Tennyson. The result was a handsome volume of forty-five pieces by leading composers of the day. All but ten of the songs were specially written. Barnby, who does not appear frequently as a composer of solo secular songs in this period, elected to set 'The Beggar Maid'. One can only regret that Barnby did not write more for the solo voice. His gift for melody combined with a faultless technique make this piece a real gem.

The tale of King Cophetua and the beggar maid is referred to several times in the works of Shakespeare and other authors. Cophetua was an African monarch and misogynist who fell victim to the charms of a fair mendicant dressed all in grey. There is some dispute as to her name. Shakespeare calls her Zenolophon and Archbishop Percy, in one of the ballads in his ***Reliques***, Penelophon. Even if he was uncertain how to pronounce her name, Cophetua married her and they lived happily ever after. There is a soulful portrayal of her in the famous Pre-Raphaelite painting of 1884 by Sir Edward Burne-Jones.

Alfred, first Baron Tennyson (1809–1892), was born into a singularly neurotic family, but began young as a poet and published a volume of juvenilia at the age of sixteen. He made a noble figure even while an undergraduate at Cambridge, with his splendid visage crowned by dark, wavy hair. Even his finely modelled hands attracted admiring comment. A future Master of Trinity remarked as the young Tennyson entered hall: 'That man must be a poet.' Although his early work had bitter critics, to whom he was morbidly sensitive, his poetical career was attended by lavish praise and the assumption of the post of poet laureate in 1850, until towards the end of the century he was, according to Ernest Rhys, 'a crowned head, removed and practically exempt from criticism'. Tennyson is a particularly Victorian figure, in the rich decoration of his poetry, its high sentiments, its pathos and its melodious lyricism as well as in his role as a literary patriarch. The verse that he originally appended to the head of his 'Dream of Fair Women' is significant:

So lifted high, the Poet at his will,
  Lets the great world flit from him, seeing all,
Higher thro' secret splendours mounting still,
  Self-poised, nor fears to fall!

Sir Joseph Barnby (1838–1896) was one of the many musical prodigies represented in this volume. An organist's son, he joined the choir at York Minster and by the age of twelve was appointed choirmaster and cathedral organist. His career was a sequence of prestigious appointments. He followed Gounod as Conductor of the Royal Albert Hall Choral Society, was Musical Director of Eton College and later became Principal of the Guildhall School of Music. The bulk of his compositions was sacred: over two hundred hymns as well as anthems, services and oratorios. His part songs include 'Sweet and Low', with poetry by Tennyson, which is to be found in *The Parlour Song Book.*

The Picture with its Face Turned to the Wall

Written and composed by J. P. SKELLY

- get - ful of good name, She lis - tened to the voice that was her
blight; From her hap - py home she fled, And tho'
tears for her were shed, No plead - ing could the way-ward one re -
rall.
rall.
a tempo
- call Now her name they nev - er speak, To for - get her they all seek, Her
a tempo

rall.
CHORUS
pic-ture hangs with face turned to the wall.
It tells the old, old sto - ry, Of
rall.
mf
sad - ness and of tears, 'Tis dead for ev - er now be - yond re -
rall.
a tempo
- call
It is of a daughter fair, Now an out-cast ev-'rywhere, The
rall.
a tempo
rall.
pic - ture with its face turned to the wall.
rit.

The Picture with its Face Turned to the Wall

1. 'Tis the picture of a fair girl,
   Now turned away from view,
   Once a mother's joy, a father's fond delight;
   But the tempting lover came,
   And forgetful of good name,
   She listened to the voice that was her blight;
   From her happy home she fled,
   And tho' tears for her were shed,
   No pleading could the wayward one recall.
   Now her name they never speak,
   To forget her they all seek,
   Her picture hangs with face turned to the wall.

CHORUS: It tells the old, old story,
Of sadness and of tears,
'Tis dead for ever now beyond recall.
It is of a daughter fair,
Now an outcast ev'rywhere,
The picture with its face turned to the wall.

2. She had home and ev'ry blessing,
   That fortune could bestow,
   And her glad young life had never known a care,
   'Till the tinsel and the gold,
   Led her from her kindred's fold,
   And she left her fond old father in despair;
   In his anger stern and deep,
   In his pride that would not sleep,
   He cast her from his heart beyond recall.
   And with frown upon his brow,
   And no pity for her now,
   He turns the picture face unto the wall.

CHORUS: It tells the old, old story, etc.

3. Now she roams the world in sorrow,
   And in her olden home,
   With dust is clad the picture and the frame,
   But the parents night and day,
   While their hair is turning gray,
   In silence still are dreaming of her name;
   In her dreams they see her blest,
   And their broken hearts attest,
   The love that lives whatever may befall.
   Yet to worldly pride they cling,
   And to them it brings a sting,
   The picture with its face turned to the wall.

CHORUS: It tells the old, old story, etc.

Inspired by a scene in the melodrama ***Blue Jeans*** by Joseph Arthur which was staged in New York in 1891 and in London seven years later, Skelly's song had a rival with a very similar name, Charles Graham's 'The Picture That Is Turned Toward the Wall'. Graham, composer of 'Two Little Girls in Blue', followed his offering with a sequel involving a reconciliation, 'Her Father Has Turned the Dear Picture Again'.

Skelly's song, in the opinion of the present editors, has a better tune than Graham's. It is irresistible in performance given lightness of touch and a properly ingenuous approach.

Joseph P. Skelly was an American plumber with musical and religious leanings. He wrote about four hundred songs but was a hopeless slave to demon drink and parted with his copyrights for trivial amounts. One publisher boasted that he paid Skelly twenty-five dollars for half-a-dozen songs, but did in fact salve his conscience by advancing money on occasion. This procedure tended to produce not only original work but copies of little-known English songs as well. Perhaps because of his improvidence and his devotion to drink Skelly was a master of the lachrymose. He wrote many hits, among them 'The Old Rustic Bridge by the Mill', 'My Pretty Red Rose', 'A Boy's Best Friend is his Mother' (which appears in *The Parlour Song Book*) and 'Strolling on the Brooklyn Bridge'.

The Volunteer Organist

Written by WILLIAM B. GRAY

Composed by HENRY LAMB

Moderato con espress.

mf

rit.

p

The preach-er in the vil-lage church one Sun-day morn-ing said, 'Our

p

or-gan-ist is ill to-day, will some-one play in-stead?' An

anx - ious look crept o'er the face of ev - 'ry per - son there, As
ea - ger - ly they watch'd to see who'd fill the va - cant chair. A
man then stag - ger'd down the aisle, whose clothes were old and torn, How
mf
strange a drunk-ard seem'd to me in church on Sun - day morn. But
when he touch'd the or - gan keys with - out a sin - gle word, The

mel - o - dy that fol low'd was the sweet est ev - er heard.
CHORUS
The scene was one I'll ne'er for-get, as long as I may live, And
Old Hundredth
p
just to see it o'er a-gain all earth-ly wealth I'd give; The
con - gre-ga - tion, all a-maz'd, the preach-er old and grey, The
or - gan and the or - gan - ist, who vol - un - teer'd to play.

The Volunteer Organist

1. The preacher in the village church one Sunday morning said,
    'Our organist is ill today, will someone play instead?'
  An anxious look crept o'er the face of ev'ry person there,
    As eagerly they watch'd to see who'd fill the vacant chair.
  A man then stagger'd down the aisle, whose clothes were old and torn,
    How strange a drunkard seem'd to me in church on Sunday morn.
  But when he touch'd the organ keys without a single word,
    The melody that follow'd was the sweetest ever heard.

CHORUS: The scene was one I'll ne'er forget, as long as I may live,
  And just to see it o'er again all earthly wealth I'd give;
  The congregation, all amaz'd, the preacher old and grey,
  The organ and the organist, who volunteer'd to play.

2. Each eye shed tears within that church, the strongest men grew pale,
    The organist, in melody, had told his own life's tale;
  The sermon of the preacher was no lesson, to compare
    With that of life's example who sat in the organ chair.
  And when the service ended, not a soul had left a seat,
    Except the poor old organist, who started toward the street.
  Along the aisle, and out the door, he slowly walked away,
    The preacher rose, and softly said, 'Good brethren, let us pray.'

CHORUS: The scene was one I'll ne'er forget, etc.

William B. Gray or Glenroy was a singer, 'the partner both in business and song' of Henry Lamb, who was really the music publisher Spaulding of Spaulding and Gray. They published this moving ballad in 1893, and its great popularity led Gray to base a play upon the theme. It also started a little genre of similar songs which are not a thousand miles away in feeling from the tales of instant conversion and repentance from the contemporary evangelistic movements. Gray also set to music 'The Picture on the Floor', a version of H. Antoine d'Arcy's poem also known as 'The Face on the Bar-Room Floor' and 'Old Jim's Christmas Hymn', both songs in the same vein as 'The Volunteer Organist'.

From the seventh bar of the introduction with the appearance of the Tin Pan Alley cadence cliché, this truly American song continues to impress its nationality upon the listener. The jaunty melodic line leads him through the scene-setting and the arrival of the protagonist to the clever bit—a quotation from the Old Hundred—curiously with the same repeated fifth at the end of each line that Weiss had used in his setting of 'The Village Blacksmith'. This song is one of the many that the musically sophisticated are wont to dismiss out of hand—quite wrongly, for in performance it is tremendously effective, a fine example of good bad art.

In the Baggage Coach Ahead

Written and composed by GUSSIE L. DAVIS

bowed- down head, The in - no - cent one commenc'd
cry - ing just then, as tho' its poor heart would break,
One an - gry man said, 'Make that child stop its noise for you're
keep- ing all of us a - wake,' 'Put it out' said an -
- oth - er, 'don't keep it in here, we've paid for our berths and want

rest,' But nev - er a word said the man with the
child, as he fon - dled it close to his breast 'Where is its
mo - ther go take it to her,' this a la - dy then soft - ly
said 'I wish that I could' was the man's sad re -
- ply, 'but she's dead, in the coach a - head.'

REFRAIN
p
While the train rolled on - ward a hus - band sat in
tears,
Think - ing of the hap-pi - ness, of just a
few short years;
For ba - by's face brings pict - ures of a
cher - ished hope that's dead
But ba - by's cries can't
wak - en her in the bag-gage coach a - head.

In the Baggage Coach Ahead

1. On a dark stormy night as a train rattled on, all the passengers had
   gone to bed,
   Except one young man with a babe on his arm, who sat there with a
   bowed-down head,
   The innocent one commenc'd crying just then, as tho' its poor heart would
   break,
   One angry man said, 'Make that child stop its noise for you're keeping
   all of us awake,'
   'Put it out', said another, 'don't keep it in here, we've paid for our berths
   and want rest,'
   But never a word said the man with the child, as he fondled it close to
   his breast—
   'Where is its mother, go take it to her,' this a lady then softly said—
   'I wish that I could,' was the man's sad reply, 'but she's dead
   in the coach ahead.'

CHORUS: While the train rolled onward a husband sat in tears,
Thinking of the happiness, of just a few short years;
For baby's face brings pictures of a cherished hope that's dead—
But baby's cries can't waken her, in the baggage coach ahead.

2. Ev'ry eye filled with tears when his story he told, of a wife who was
   faithful and true,
   He told how he'd saved up his earnings for years, just to build up a
   home for two,
   How, when heaven had sent them this sweet little babe, their young happy
   lives were blessed,
   In tears he broke down when he mentioned her name, and in tears tried
   to tell the rest,

   Ev'ry woman arose to assist with the child, there were mothers and wives
   on that train,
   And soon was the little one sleeping in peace, with no thoughts of sorrow
   and pain.
   Next morn' at a station he bade all goodbye, 'God bless you,' he softly said—
   Each one had a story to tell in their home, of the baggage coach ahead.

CHORUS: While the train rolled onward a husband sat in tears, etc.

The sad tale behind this song of 1896 is well attested. Unlike most effusions from Tin Pan Alley, this piece is rooted in a real moment of tragedy. Gussie L. Davis was a Negro porter on the actual train of the story, although he adapted the details somewhat. The father's reply to passengers protesting about his noisy children, 'Their mother is in a casket in the baggage coach ahead,'—a complaint-stopper if ever there was one—was first of all the inspiration for a poem written by Frank Archer, a fellow worker on the same train as Davis. The latter reduced the children to one baby, and that little girl, apparently, was to become Mrs Nellie Klapmeyer who died in Kansas City some years ago.

Gussie L. Davis wrote other songs grave and gay, among them 'The Lighthouse by the Sea', but only this one piece has any celebrity today. He is said to have been a very modest and retiring figure.

It is a large measure of the charm of the songs of Tin Pan Alley that they treat the most gruesome and least lighthearted subjects in an utterly naïve and winningly tuneful way. This song is no exception to the rule. No railroad freight carriage, let alone one shipping a coffin, ever promoted so gracious and well-made a melody. If the words are taken away what is left is a slightly pedestrian setting for the verse, but this is followed by a waltz that suggests chandeliers and ball-gowns rather than bereavement. It really is a seductive composition that deserves a second and third hearing.

Hope Springs Eternal

Kingdom Coming (The Year of Jubilo)

Written and composed by HENRY CLAY WORK

took his hat and leff ber-ry sud-den an' I spec he's run a - way,
CHORUS
De mas - sa run, ha, ha! De dar - kies stay, ho, ho! It
De mas - sa run, ha, ha! De dar - kies stay, ho, ho! It
De mas - sa run, ha, ha! De dar - kies stay, ho, ho! It
De mas - sa run, ha, ha! De dar - kies stay, ho, ho! It
mus' be now de king-dom co-min', an' de Year ob Ju - bi - lo!
mus' be now de king-dom co-min', an' de Year ob Ju - bi - lo!
mus' be now de king-dom co-min', an' de Year ob Ju - bi - lo!
mus' be now de king-dom co-min', an' de Year ob Ju - bi - lo!

Kingdom Coming

1. Say, darkies, hab you seen de massa,
   Wid de muffstash on his face,
   Go 'long de road some time dis mornin
   Like he gwine to leab de place?
   He's seen a smoke, way up de ribber,
   Whar de Linkum gum-boats lay;
   He took his hat and lef berry sudden,
   An' I spec he's run away,

CHORUS: De massa run, ha, ha!
De darkies stay, ho, ho!
It mus' be now de kingdom comin',
An' de Year ob Jubilo!

2. He's six foot one way, two foot tudder,
   An' he weigh tree hundred pound;
   His coat so big, he couldn't pay de tailor,
   An' it won't go half way round;
   He drill so much dey call him Cap'an,
   An' he get so dreffful tanned,
   I spec he try an' fool dem Yankees
   For to tink he's contraband,

CHORUS: De massa run, ha, ha! etc.

3. De darkies feel so lonesome libing
   In de log-house on de lawn,
   Dey move dar tings to massa's parlour,
   For to keep it while he's gone.
   Dar's wine and cider in de kitchen,
   An' de darkies dey'll hab some;
   I spose dey'll all be confiscated
   When de Linkum sojers come,

CHORUS: De massa run, ha, ha! etc.

4. De oberseer he make us trouble,
   An' he dribe us round a spell;
   We lock him up in de smoke-house cellar,
   Wid de key trown in de well:
   De whip is lost, de hancuff broken,
   But de massa'll hab his pay;
   He's ole enough, big enough, ought to know better
   Dan to went an' run away,

CHORUS: De massa run, ha, ha! etc.

A tremendously infectious melody of 1862, this version is taken from *The Tonic Sol-Fa Times* of 1868. There it was set out in basic sol-fa, a real relic of the nineteenth century.

Kingdom Coming (*The Year of Jubilo*)

'Kingdom Coming' is one of the Unionist songs that Work flung into the propaganda battles of the Civil War along with 'Song of a Thousand Years', 'God Save the Union', 'Grafted into the Army' and, most famous of all, 'Marching through Georgia'. Even today, it is said, they fall discordantly upon Southern ears.

Henry Clay Work (1832–1884), born in Middleton, Conn., was the son of an Abolitionist whose home was a station on the famous 'underground railroad' that assisted in the escape of thousands of slaves from the South. Young Work was caught up in his father's enthusiasm and became a fervent Abolitionist and Unionist himself. Trained as a printer, he taught himself music and is reported to have set his songs directly in music-type. He started to compose songs, and 'Kingdom Coming' was his first big success. After sterling musical service in the Civil War—he must have been worth several regiments in the Northern cause—he demobilised his muse and settled down to write more domestic ballads. Not the least of his remarkable attributes was his beard, one of the most luxuriant in a conspicuously hairy age.

Work is a melodist worthy to stand beside Stephen Foster, for his plain, direct words and fresh, memorable music have a satisfying unity, largely because they are the product of a single mind. *The Parlour Song Book* contains three other much-loved ballads of his, 'Grandfather's Clock', 'Come Home, Father' (Work was a Prohibitionist, too) and 'Ring the Bell, Watchman'.

Oh, How Delightful!

Written by ARTHUR SKETCHLEY

Composed by JAMES L. MOLLOY

p
gai - ly now with glee. From morn till night im - pris - on'd
p
here, Pass'd we our days in gloom and fear;
No joys to cheer us, no de - light, All was
rall.
drea - ry, noth - ing bright; Now, how de - light - ful,
rall.
now, how en - tranc - ing, From this drear thral - dom soon to be

free! With wild - est joy, then, my heart is dan - cing,
Danc - ing so gai - ly now with glee. Ah!
p
p leggiero
ah! my heart is danc - ing now with
p
glee, Ah! ah!
cresc.
my heart is danc - ing now with glee.
rit.

Oh, How Delightful!

1. Oh, how delightful, oh, how entrancing,
   From this drear thraldom soon to be free!
With wildest joy, then, my heart is dancing,
   Dancing so gaily now with glee.
From morn till night imprison'd here,
   Pass'd we our days in gloom and fear;
No joys to cheer us, no delight,
   All was dreary, nothing bright;
Now, how delightful, now, how entrancing,
   From this drear thraldom soon to be free!
With wildest joy, then, my heart is dancing,
   Dancing so gaily now with glee.
Ah! ah! my heart is dancing now with glee,
Ah! ah! my heart is dancing now with glee.

2. Oft when dark shadows are o'er us creeping,
   And check the throbbing of youthful hearts,
Hope, like a sunbeam, watch near us keeping,
   Breaks thro' the gloom and joy imparts.
No longer shall we droop and pine,
   In dreary hours, our lives away,
When clouds are darkest, oft doth shine,
   Softly and brightly, hope's cheering ray.
Yes, how delightful, yes, how entrancing,
   From this drear thraldom soon to be free! etc.

This vivacious song comes from an operetta, *The Student's Frolic*, and whatever the original thraldom in that obviously comic piece, the public at large took it to mean the thraldom of Life from which one would escape to Glory. Here we have the archetypal waltz-song, even to the extent of the voice line being instrumental in character. It is quite charming, if perhaps a bit giggle-provoking in the passages of mock-opera.

'Arthur Sketchley' was the *nom de plume* of George Rose (1817–1882), comic writer and entertainer. After a period as a custom-house clerk he entered the Church of England and fell subject to the doctrinal doubts fashionable at the time, changing his faith to Roman Catholicism. He then took up a literary life. He invented and represented on stage the salty character of Mrs Brown, an illiterate old woman whose thoughts on myriad topics of the day eventually filled thirty-two volumes. Rose's travels as an entertainer took him to the United States, Europe, South Africa, Australia, New Zealand and India. He never married, grew immensely fat and perished of heart disease.

James Lyman Molloy (1837–1909), one of the best vocal composers of his time, was educated at the Catholic university in Dublin, afterwards in London, Paris and Bonn. He became a barrister in the Middle Temple, but his fine singing voice and his facility in song-writing led him largely to abandon the law for music. He wrote three operettas, from one of which came his first really successful song, 'Beer, Beer, Beautiful Beer' which appears to have a different tune to the one we know today. With John L. Hatton he edited a collection of Irish folk songs and produced about a hundred ballads including that theme song of the parlour 'Love's Old Sweet Song' (in *The Parlour Song Book*) and such favourites as 'The Kerry Dance' and 'Thursday', which appears in this volume.

The Deathless Army

Written by FRED E. WEATHERLY

Composed by H. TROTÈRE

heard the drums and the trum - pets' blare, The gal - lant troops were
must' - ring there, The flower of our brave old ar - my,
più rall.
a tempo
f più rall.
a tempo
legato
Stal - wart boys and vet' - rans old, Side by side in their
red and gold, With a cheer and a smile went rank and file, In the
f marcato
mf col voce
f marcato

rall.
mf a tempo
van of our brave old ar - my. March-ing for the dear old
mf a tempo
coun - try, March-ing a-way to war, With the
hearts they love be-hind them, And the flag they love, be-
- fore March-ing for the dear old coun - try, March-ing a-way to
f
mf
marcato rit.
molto rit.
war, With the hearts they love be-hind them, And the
colla voce
rall.

lunga
Allegro moderato
flag they love, be - fore.
marcato
mf
decresc. e rit.
p
mf Gravamente
'Twas deep still night in the ci - ty square,
lento col voce
p
Hushed were the drums and the trum - pets' blare, But a phan - tom host was
rall.
march - ing there, In the steps of the brave old ar - my!

Più animato e misterioso
Solemnly, silently through the night, Grim set faces and
Più animato e ten.
cresc. e accel.
eyes so bright, As heroes look when they march to fight, At the
rall.
f
mf
Moderato e dolce
head of a mighty army. And then I knew in the
rall.
f
ff
mf
Moderato col voce
Ped.
cresc.
still night-tide, What men were must'ring side by side,
cresc.
f con energia
They were the men who had fought and died In the ranks of our brave old
f marcato

dolce
ar - my. And their gal - lant swords may bro - ken lie, Their
col voce
allarg.
a tempo
mf cresc.
bones may bleach 'neath an a - lien sky, But their souls, I know, will
poco rit.
a tempo
mf cresc.
ritard.
a tempo
molto rit.
ne - ver die, They march in a death - less ar - my!
ritard.
col voce
molto rit.
p
March-ing for the dear old coun - try, Lead - ing us for e - ver -
pp stacc.
- more, For the souls of the he - roes die not In the
cresc.
cresc.

land that they a - dore!
March-ing for the dear old
cresc.
f
coun - try,
Lead-ing us for ev - er - more.
For the
rit
molto rit.
lunga
souls of the he - roes die not
In the land that they a-
Allegro
-dore.
ff
fff

The Deathless Army

1. 'Twas golden noon in the city square,
   I heard the drums and the trumpets' blare,
   The gallant troops were must'ring there.
   The flower of our brave old army,
   Stalwart boys and vet'rans old,
   Side by side in their red and gold,
   With a cheer and a smile went rank and file,
   In the van of our brave old army.

CHORUS: Marching for the dear old country,
Marching away to war,
With the hearts they love behind them,
And the flag they love, before.

2. 'Twas deep still night in the city square,
   Hushed were the drums and the trumpets' blare,
   But a phantom host was marching there,
   In the steps of the brave old army!
   Solemnly, silently through the night,
   Grim set faces and eyes so bright,
   As heroes look when they march to fight,
   At the head of a mighty army.

CHORUS: Marching for the dear old country, etc.

3. And then I knew in the still night-tide,
   What men were must'ring side by side,
   They were the men who had fought and died
   In the ranks of our brave old army.
   And their gallant swords may broken lie,
   Their bones may bleach 'neath an alien sky,
   But their souls, I know, will never die,
   They march in a deathless army.

CHORUS: Marching for the dear old country,
Leading us for evermore,
For the souls of the heroes die not
In the land that they adore!

The jingoistic chorus of this song ensures its survival wherever two or three rugby players are gathered together. Anyone who performs this piece in accordance with the exhaustive directions will arrive, presumably, at what the composer had in mind. Such attention to minute detail of performance is considered pedantic nowadays, but may lead to a more authentic, if perhaps less acceptable, rendering. Trotère does not miss a trick in his setting. Observe the scene-setting fanfare with drums and trumpets specified. The relentless march rhythm and the heavy tread of the phantom boots in the second verse are points to notice, as is the chromatic acceleration away from the gloom into realisation's bright light in the third verse where the revelation is accentuated by a *colla voce* in the bass against a shimmering of strings in the treble. This soon gives way again, however, to the staccato march rhythm of the chorus which exhorts us to wipe our eyes and pick up our feet.

In its time 'The Deathless Army' of 1891 was enough of a household name to form the basis of an English music-hall song in which Little Tich declared as a territorial soldier:

> If ever I go to war, I'll drive the enemy barmy,
> Hi, Hi! Never say die!
> I'm one of the deathless army.

The life and work of that ubiquitous parlour lyricist Fred E. (Frederic Edward) Weatherly (1848–1929) appear in *The Parlour Song Book.* He was a cheerful if somewhat self-satisfied lawyer who graduated by way of undergraduate poems and verses for Christmas cards to producing eminently singable words for practically the whole song-composing community in late nineteenth-century England. There are two more of his songs in this book, 'The Holy City' and 'Thursday' on pages 181 and 238, and three others in its companion volume, 'The Old Brigade', 'Nancy Lee' and 'Auntie'. He also wrote such lasting pieces as 'Danny Boy' and 'The Roses of Picardy', and produced English versions of *Cavalleria Rusticana* and *Pagliacci* that are still used today.

H. Trotère had a far more mundane name in reality. He was Henry Trotter (1855–?), born in London, who attained a modest celebrity as a composer of songs.

The Holy City

Written by FRED E. WEATHERLY

Composed by STEPHEN ADAMS

p

1. Last night I lay a-sleep-ing, There came a dream so fair, I

p

stood in old Je-ru-sa-lem Be-side the tem-ple there. I

heard the child-ren sing-ing, And e-ver as they sang Me-

thought the voice of An-gels From Heav'n in an-swer rang; Me-

mf *cre — — scen — — — do*

cantabile
- thought the voice of An - gels From
f
rall.
Heav'n in an - swer rang, Je -
dim.
a tempo
- ru - sa-lem! Je - ru - sa-lem! Lift up your gates and
p
cresc.
sing, Ho - san - na in_the high - est! Ho -
mf
f
colla voce
- san - na_ to your King!
a tempo
ff

2. And
then me-thought my dream was chang'd, The streets no long - er rang,
Hush'd were the glad Ho-san-nas The lit - tle chil-dren sang. The
sun grew dark with mys - te - ry. The morn was cold and chill, As the
p
sha - dow of a cross a-rose Up - on a lone - ly hill, As the
mf
cre - scen - do

cantabile
sha - dow of a cross a - rose Up -
f
rall.
a tempo
- on a lone - ly hill. Je - ru - sa-lem! Je -
dim.
p
- ru - sa lem! Hark! how the An - gels sing, Ho -
cresc.
- san - na in the high - est, Ho - san - na to your
mf
f
colla voce
a tempo
King.
ff

affret. poco a poco
3. And once a-gain the scene was chang'd, New
dim.
pp
earth there seem'd to be, I saw the Ho-ly Ci-ty Be-
-side the tide-less sea; The light of God was on its streets, The
cre - - scen -
cantabile
gates were o-pen wide, And all who would might
do
f
rall.
en - - ter, And no one was de -
dim.

a tempo
nied. No need of moon Or
p
stars by night, or sun to shine by
cre – – scen –
affret.
day, It was the new Je –
do
allargando
– ru – sa lem That would not pass a –
cre scen
grandioso
way. It was the new Je - ru - sa lem That
– – do
f

rall.
a tempo
would not pass a - way. "Je - ru - sa - lem! Je
p
- ru - sa lem! Sing for the night is o'er! Ho -
cresc.
- san - na in the high - est, Ho - san - na for e - ver -
mf
f
more! Ho - san - na in the high - est, Ho -
ad lib.
f
colla voce
- san - na for e - ver more!"
ff

The Holy City

1. Last night I lay asleeping,
   There came a dream so fair,
   I stood in old Jerusalem
   Beside the temple there.
   I heard the children singing,
   And ever as they sang
   Methought the voice of Angels
   From Heav'n in answer rang;
   Methought the voice of Angels
   From Heav'n in answer rang,

   Jerusalem! Jerusalem!
   Lift up your gates and sing,
   Hosanna in the highest!
   Hosanna to your King!

2. And then methought my dream was chang'd,
   The streets no longer rang,
   Hush'd were the glad Hosannas
   The little children sang.
   The sun grew dark with mystery,
   The morn was cold and chill,
   As the shadow of a cross arose
   Upon a lonely hill,
   As the shadow of a cross arose
   Upon a lonely hill.

   Jerusalem! Jerusalem!
   Hark! how the Angels sing,
   Hosanna in the highest,
   Hosanna to your King.

3. And once again the scene was chang'd,
   New earth there seem'd to be,
   I saw the Holy City
   Beside the tideless sea;
   The light of God was on its streets,
   The gates were open wide,
   And all who would might enter,
   And no one was denied.
   No need of moon or stars by night,
   Or sun to shine by day,
   It was the new Jerusalem
   That would not pass away,
   It was the new Jerusalem
   That would not pass away.

Jerusalem! Jerusalem!
Sing for the night is o'er!
Hosanna in the highest,
Hosanna for evermore!
Hosanna in the highest,
Hosanna for evermore!

The stirring invocation to the holy city to lift up its gates and sing has the same quasi-religious force as that other semi-anthem adopted by the Women's Institutes of Britain, 'Jerusalem'. 'The Holy City' attained enormous celebrity, for despite its sacred connotations it was promoted with some commercial acumen. Edward Lloyd the tenor reported to the *Musical Times* in 1899: 'It sells at the rate of 50,000 copies per annum. In Montreal I was engaged to sing four times in one month at a fee of 250 guineas each concert, *on condition* that I sang "The Holy City" on each occasion.'

Musically, the song is superb. It is *religioso* but with a fine muscular chorus that must have echoed around many a bathroom since 1892. Take note of the harmonic progression for the opening of the gates in the third verse and the careful syllabic setting of the name of the Holy City. The fact that the highest note of the piece comes on the very word 'highest' is no coincidence with a composer of the calibre of Stephen Adams.

There are some notes on Fred E. Weatherly on page 180. 'Stephen Adams' was the song-writing pseudonym of the baritone Michael Maybrick (1844–1913) for whom he wrote sea-songs remarkably suited to his fine voice. Another infant phenomenon—there are many in this book—a pianist and organist, he was appointed to the manual of St Peter's, Liverpool, when he was fourteen. Maurice Willson Disher records: 'While still of school age he wore the morning coat and top hat of a professional man and appeared with great dignity on concert platforms', and a typically Victorian picture he must have made. While training at Leipzig he discovered the potential of his powerful voice, but his talent for composition was only recognised when he was writing songs to exploit himself. As well as his nautical ballads he had a talent for rousing sacred songs, of which 'The Star of Bethlehem' and 'The Holy City' are good examples.

The Emerald Isle

The Meeting of the Waters

Written by THOMAS MOORE, music traditional

bright wa – ters meet. Oh! the last rays of feel – ing and

life must de – part Ere the bloom of that val – ley shall

lentando
cresc.
fade from my heart! Ere the bloom of that val-ley shall fade from my heart!
mf

The Meeting of the Waters

1. There is not in the wide world a valley so sweet
   As that vale in whose bosom the bright waters meet.
   Oh! the last rays of feeling and life must depart
   Ere the bloom of that valley shall fade from my heart!

2. Yet it was not that Nature had shed o'er the scene
   Her purest of crystal and brightest of green;
   'Twas not the soft magic of streamlet or hill;
   Oh! no—it was something more exquisite still!

3. 'Twas that friends, the beloved of my bosom were near,
   Who made every dear scene of enchantment more dear;
   And who felt how the best charms of Nature improve
   When we see them reflected from looks that we love.

4. Sweet vale of Avoca! how calm could I rest
   In thy bosom of shade, with the friends I love best,
   Where the storms which we feel in this cold world should cease,
   And our hearts, like thy waters, be mingled in peace!

Thomas Moore's *Irish Melodies* are a foundation stone of nineteenth-century parlour balladry. In style and tone they anticipated the sweet melancholy of untold reams of Victorian sheet music, and even their financial success was a harbinger of the dividends that were to flow from the sentimental and nostalgic songs of the mid-century and later.

In 1807 Moore was out of favour with his royal patron, the Prince of Wales ('Prinny', later Prince Regent). He had returned from a tour of the United States which he proceeded to castigate in his *Odes and Epistles*, and had recently been involved in an undignified farce of a duel with a critic. He was living largely on his wits when he began to collect folk airs, write new, unexceptional words to them and publish the results as *Irish Melodies*, the music arranged by Sir John Stevenson. Many of them were not Irish at all in origin but English or Scottish. However, they caught the popular taste and helped to inculcate a fresh, romantic view of 'Erin' as well as provide Moore with a secure income. For the next twenty-seven years the *Melodies* were published in ten volumes of twelve songs apiece (except for the last which contained fourteen), and the poet collected a hundred guineas a song, a total of £12,810, a really sizeable sum at that time. He also mined the same vein, too, in his *National Airs* (which contains 'Oft in the Stilly Night') of 1815 and his *Sacred Songs* of 1816.

The fame of the *Melodies* was not confined to Britain and America. They held an important place in European music, too. Beethoven set some of them, and Berlioz produced his *Irlande* (neuf mélodies pour une et deux voix sur des traductions de Thomas Moore) in 1829. It is obvious that Moore hit upon a formula that found an instant response in early nineteenth-century society. These romantic, improved national airs in accomplished settings by Stevenson and, towards the end of the series, also by Sir Henry Bishop, reflect the polite taste of the time. Leisurely and genteel, they bring into the home the alluring fragrance of the countryside, innocent of manure. 'The Meeting of the Waters', based on the air 'The Old Head of Dennis', has been so smoothed and polished and been provided with such sophisticated accompaniments that it has lost a great deal of its ethnic quality. Finally, it can stand comparison with the more urbanely conceived ballads of no rustic pretensions at all—a kind of Petit Trianon to the Versailles of 'To Anthea'. There is another ***Irish Melody***, 'Believe Me if All Those Endearing Young Charms' in a duet setting on page 250.

Thomas Moore (1779–1852), the Irish poet, had an immensely varied and colourful life which is summarised in the notes to another ***Irish Melody***, 'The Last Rose of Summer' in ***The Parlour Song Book***. He was in an ideal position to promote the songs in London. During the period of their introduction Moore was known to good society less as a poet than as a singer and pianist. Even before coming to London, while he was at Trinity College, Dublin, he had caused a sensation with his sprightly and charming performances. Lord Moira was his patron, and with his help Moore captured the hearts of the English aristocracy who were quick to welcome into their drawing-rooms the brilliant and romantic young Irishman.

Years later Moore was to be criticised for his popularisation of a false image of Ireland. He himself would probably have been astonished by the curious forms the idea of Ould Oireland assumed by the end of the century when songwriters on both sides of the Atlantic were grinding out ballad after ballad replete with shamrocks, shillelaghs, leprechauns and the rest of the paraphernalia proper to parlour Irishry. Even today it is not unknown for the Irish themselves cheerfully to perpetuate the great loony cod and spread that flowing Celtic mist wider still.

Kathleen Mavourneen

Composed by F. N. CROUCH

horn of the hun - ter is heard on the hill, The
lark from her light wing the bright dew is sha - king
Kath-leen Mav-our-neen! what slum - b'ring still?
mf
2. Oh! hast thou for - got-ten, how
soon we must se-ver? Oh! hast thou for - got - ten this
mf

day we must part, It may be for years, and it
colla voce
may be for - ev-er! Oh! why art thou si - lent thou
p
voice of my heart? It may be for years and it
cresc.
may be for - ev - er! Then why art thou si - lent
Kath-leen Mav-our - neen?
mf

Kathleen Mavourneen

- rise in thy beau-ty, thou star of my night.
slantando
a tempo
mf con amore
4. Mav - our - neen, Mav-
rall.
pp
- our-neen, my sad tears are fall-ing, To think that from
mf
fz
E - rin and thee I must part, it may be for
pp

years, and it may be for ev-er! Then why art thou
semplice
f
si - lent thou voice of my heart? It may be for
mf
mf
mf
years, and it may be for ev-er! Then why art thou si - lent
rall.
Kath-leen Mav-our-neen?
p

Kathleen Mavourneen

1. Kathleen Mavourneen! the grey dawn is breaking,
   The horn of the hunter is heard on the hill,
   The lark from her light wing the bright dew is shaking,
   Kathleen Mavourneen! what slumb'ring still?

2. Oh! hast thou forgotten, how soon we must sever?
   Oh! hast thou forgotten this day we must part,
   It may be for years, and it may be for ever!
   Oh! why art thou silent thou voice of my heart?
   It may be for years, and it may be for ever!
   Then why art thou silent Kathleen Mavourneen

3. Kathleen Mavourneen! Awake from thy slumbers,
   The blue mountains glow in the sun's golden light,
   Ah! where is the spell that once hung on my numbers,
   Arise in thy beauty, thou star of my night.
   Arise in thy beauty, thou star of my night.

4. Mavourneen, Mavourneen, my sad tears are falling,
   To think that from Erin and thee I must part,
   It may be for years, and it may be for ever!
   Then why art thou silent thou voice of my heart?
   It may be for years, and it may be for ever!
   Then why art thou silent Kathleen Mavourneen?

There is a little mystery surrounding the provenance of this song which remained a much-loved Gem for over sixty years. Originally, according to M. Willson Disher's *Victorian Song*, the words appeared in 1835 under the name of Julia Crawford who was apparently the wife of the composer F. N. Crouch. However, some editions attribute the whole song to Crouch and others the lyric to Mrs Annie Barry Crawford. The piece had already appeared in Crouch's *Echoes of the Lake* in Britain by the time it was first published in the United States in 1840.

Frederick William Nicholls Crouch (1808–1896) came of a musical family and was playing in the band of the Royal Coburg Theatre in London by the age of nine. After a couple of years at sea he joined the orchestra of Drury Lane Theatre as a cellist. Also a singer in the choirs of St Paul's Cathedral and Westminster Abbey, he received training at the Royal Academy of Music and became a member of Queen Adelaide's private orchestra. His non-musical interests included engraving and he is said to have been the originator of the process of zincography. 'Kathleen Mavourneen' was the product of a passion for Irish songs and legends and he lectured on this subject. In 1849 he went to America and found a position as cellist at the Astor Place Theatre. He settled in Portland, Maine, where he died, having also lived in Philadelphia, Washington, Richmond and Baltimore. Throughout the Civil War he served as a trumpeter in the Confederate Army. Also a naturalist and a sportsman, he had cages full of snakes at his Portland home and was celebrated for the game dinners he served his friends. Crouch wrote many other songs and two operas, but 'Kathleen Mavourneen' is the only work of his remembered today. He composed a sequel to it, an 'answer' entitled 'Dermot Asthore' with words by Desmond Ryan.

The Rose of Tralee

Written by E. MORDAUNT SPENCER Composed by CHARLES W. GLOVER

foun - tain That stands in the beau - ti - ful vale of Tra - lee: She was
love - ly and fair as the rose of the sum - mer, Yet 'twas not her
beau - ty a - lone that won me, Oh, no! 'twas the truth, in her
sf
p
eye ev - er dawn - ing, That made me love Ma - ry the Rose of Tra
- lee.
rall.
D.C.

The Rose of Tralee

1. The pale moon was rising above the green mountain,
   The sun was declining beneath the blue sea,
   When I stray'd with my love to the pure crystal fountain
   That stands in the beautiful vale of Tralee:

CHORUS: She was lovely and fair as the rose of the summer,
Yet 'twas not her beauty alone that won me,
Oh, no! 'twas the truth in her eye ever dawning,
That made me love Mary, the Rose of Tralee.

2. The cool shades of evening their mantle were spreading,
   And Mary all smiling was list'ning to me,
   The moon thro' the valley her pale ray was shedding
   When I won the heart of the Rose of Tralee:

CHORUS: She was lovely and fair as the rose of the summer, etc.

This charming little piece is so completely in the folk-song idiom that few people not knowing its authorship would credit a nineteenth-century song-writer with its composition. The restrained range and the singing line perfectly turned for the voice are the hallmarks of a piece polished for centuries on the rough edges of bucolic vocal chords. They are not often met in the parlour and bring a touch of welcome freshness. There is a remarkably good arrangement of this song made many years after its composition by Roger Quilter.

Charles William Glover (1806–1863), born in London, was the brother of the better-known Stephen Glover whose 'What Are the Wild Waves Saying?' is to be found elsewhere in this volume. C. W. Glover was violinist in the orchestras of the Drury Lane and Covent Garden Theatres and became musical director of the Queen's Theatre. His output of songs, duets and instrumental music was consigned to oblivion a century ago, with the notable exception of 'The Rose of Tralee' and perhaps 'Tis Hard to Give the Hand Where the Heart Can Never Be' for its title alone.

Killarney

Written by EDMUND FALCONER

Composed by M. W. BALFE

rall.
ev'-ry where; Footprints leaves on ma-ny strands But her home is
colla parte
dim. pp a tempo
sure-ly there! An-gels fold their wings and rest In that E-den
riten.
pp a tempo
cresc.
f
of the west, Beau-ty's home Kil-lar-ney, Heav'n's re-flex Kil-lar-ney.
f
mf
cresc.
f
D.S.

Killarney

1. By Killarney's lakes and fells
   Em'rald isles and winding bays;
   Mountain paths and woodland dells,
   Mem'ry ever fondly strays.
   Bounteous nature loves all lands,
   Beauty wanders ev'rywhere;
   Footprints leaves on many strands
   But her home is surely there!
   Angels fold their wings and rest
   In that Eden of the west,
   Beauty's home Killarney,
   Heav'n's reflex Killarney.

2. No place else can charm the eye
   With such bright and varied tints,
   Ev'ry rock that you pass by
   Verdure broiders or besprints.
   Virgin there the green grass grows,
   Ev'ry morn springs natal day,
   Bright hued berries daff the snows,
   Smiling winter's frown away.
   Angels often pausing there
   Doubt if Eden were more fair,
   Beauty's home Killarney,
   Heav'n's reflex Killarney.

In many ways this is *the* Irish song. Melodically and harmonically it is most people's idea of 'pure' Hibernian music, for it is smooth and shapely with more of a 'feeling of movement' than actual movement—a kind of musical blarney, in fact. The words, however, are decidedly odd. Despite its enormous popularity, the song has some singularly unfelicitous lines including the last one, and one wonders in which Irish dictionary the poet found the verbs 'to besprint' and 'to daff'.

The real name of Edmund Falconer (1814–1879), actor and playwright, was Edmund O'Rourke. His theatrical career opened in Ireland, but he moved to England to act in stock companies. His London debut was in his own play *The Cagot, or Heart for Heart*, and this was successful enough to lead to more commissions for plays and more parts to act. He was appointed manager of the Lyceum and later joint lessee of Drury Lane Theatre, and put on more of his own plays at both theatres. After failing abjectly with the works of another dramatist—William Shakespeare—he crossed the Atlantic and opened at the Olympic Theatre in New York City, acting, of course, in one of his own plays. After three years in the States he returned to London and put on the play popularly known as *Killarney*. It is to Falconer's impersonations of bucolic Irish peasants that we owe, in large part, the stereotype of that semi-comic sentimental figure. He married thrice. His last bride, an American lady, was tougher than her predecessors and survived him.

Michael William Balfe (1808–1870), another émigré from Dublin, did not quite adopt the same role of professional Irishman as did Falconer, perhaps because in music a continental persona was more prestigious. For a while Balfe called himself Signor Balfo. Until the advent of Arthur Sullivan, Balfe was by far the best-known of theatrical composers working in Britain. His career is summarised in *The Parlour Song Book*, which prints three other songs of his, 'The Dream' ('I Dreamt that I Dwelt in Marble Halls'), 'Come into the Garden, Maud' and 'Excelsior!' Balfe's gift for melody complemented the vivacity of his character and his songs still have enormous charm.

Come Back to Erin

Written and composed by CLARIBEL

Sure, when we lent ye to
beau - ti - ful Eng - land, Lit - tle we thought of the lone win - ter days,
Lit - tle we thought of the hush of the star shine O - ver the moun - tain, the
Animato
Bluffs and the Brays! Then come back to E - rin, Mav-
f
p
mf
6
6

-our - neen, Mav-our - neen, Come back a-gain to the
land of thy birth, Come back to E - rin, Mav-
rit.
cresc
our - neen, Mav-our - neen, And its Kil-lar - ney shall ring with our
molto cresc.
f
8va
mirth.
mf
8va
D.C.

Come Back to Erin

1. Come back to Erin, Mavourneen, Mavourneen,
   Come back Aroon, to the land of thy birth,
Come with the shamrocks and springtime, Mavourneen,
   And its Killarney shall ring with our mirth.
Sure, when we lent ye to beautiful England,
   Little we thought of the lone winter days,
Little we thought of the hush of the star shine,
   Over the mountain, the Bluffs and the Brays!
Then come back to Erin, Mavourneen, Mavourneen,
Come back again to the land of thy birth,
Come back to Erin, Mavourneen, Mavourneen,
And its Killarney shall ring with our mirth.

2. Over the green sea, Mavourneen, Mavourneen,
   Long shone the white sail that bore thee away,
Riding the white waves that fair summer mornin'
   Just like a Mayflower afloat on the bay.
O but my heart sank when clouds came between us,
   Like a grey curtain the rain falling down,
Hid from my sad eyes the path o'er the ocean,
   Far, far away where my colleen had flown.
Then come back to Erin, Mavourneen, Mavourneen,
Come back again to the land of thy birth,
Come back to Erin, Mavourneen, Mavourneen,
And its Killarney shall ring with our mirth.

3. O may the Angels, a-wakin' and sleepin'
   Watch o'er my bird in the land far away,
And it's my pray'rs will consign to their keepin'
   Care o' my jewel by night and by day.
When by the fire side, I watch the bright embers,
   Then all my heart flies to England and thee,
Cravin' to know if my darlin' remembers,
   Or if her thoughts may be crossin' to me.
Then come back to Erin, Mavourneen, Mavourneen,
Come back again to the land of thy birth,
Come back to Erin, Mavourneen, Mavourneen,
And its Killarney shall ring with our mirth.

Understandably Claribel's greatest hit, this ballad of 1866 does not even pay lip service to any folk or Irish idiom in the setting, although there is an obligatory dropping of the 'g's in the words. It had enormous popularity on both sides of the Atlantic, and there is a recording of a barrel organ made by Imhof and Mukle in London which has survived to wheeze out the song today as it was interpreted over a hundred years ago. The *ritornello* passages are hurried through helter-skelter to get back to the real meat of the piece, the tune—and a very good tune it is, too.

'Claribel' was Mrs Charlotte Alington Barnard (1830–1869) who had a short but musically very prolific life entirely in tune with the sentimental tastes of her time. Although she was English, Claribel had immense celebrity in the United States, particularly for her 'Take Back the Heart That Thou Gavest Me', but even this was eclipsed by 'Come Back to Erin'. Despite the obvious parlour character of the ballad many people thought of it as a folk song. There are more notes on Mrs Barnard in *The Parlour Song Book*, together with her affecting 'Oh Mother! Take the Wheel Away'. She probably chose her pseudonym from Tennyson's early poem, 'Claribel, A Melody', which begins:

Where Claribel low-lieth
   The breezes pause and die,

and finishes:

   Her song the lintwhite swelleth,
The clear-voiced mavis dwelleth,
   The callow throstle lispeth,
The slumbrous wave outwelleth,
   The babbling runnel crispeth,
The hollow grot replieth
   Where Claribel low-lieth.

A clear case of lisping in numbers.

Sweet Rosie O'Grady

Written and composed by MAUDE NUGENT

she's the sweet-est lit - tle Rose the gar - den ev - er grew.
rall.
CHORUS Valse
Sweet Ro sie O' Gra - dy, My
f
dear lit - tle Rose, She's my stea - dy
la - dy, Most ev'- ry - one knows,

And when we are mar - ried,
How happy we'll be;
I love sweet Ro - sie O' Gra - dy, And Ro - sie O'
Gra - dy loves me.
1
2
me.
D.C.
D.C.

Sweet Rosie O'Grady

1. Just down around the corner of the street where I reside,
   There lives the cutest little girl that I have ever spied;
 Her name is Rose O'Grady and, I don't mind telling you,
   That she's the sweetest little Rose the garden ever grew.

CHORUS: Sweet Rosie O'Grady,
My dear little Rose,
She's my steady lady,
'Most ev'ryone knows,
And when we are married,
How happy we'll be;
I love sweet Rosie O'Grady,
And Rosie O'Grady loves me.

2. I never shall forget the day she promised to be mine,
   As we set telling love tales, in the golden summer time.
 'Twas on her finger that I placed a small engagement ring,
   While in the trees, the little birds this song they seemed to sing!

CHORUS: Sweet Rosie O'Grady, etc.

Compared to the carefully composed ballads of Claribel and Molloy, this song is as natural as the Rose it hymns.

The sheet music bears the name and picture of the singer and dancer Maude Nugent of 'The Abbey' on Eighth Avenue in New York City, run by Johnny Reilly. Although there is no firm evidence for the belief, it is highly likely that most of the credit for the song should go to Maude Nugent's husband, the lyric-writer William (Billy) Jerome (1865–1932). Born at Cornwall on the Hudson River, his theatrical life as an actor and singer began early: at eighteen he was already in a Minstrel show. He later became a music publisher, supplied verses for many song-writers including Harry von Tilzer and collaborated in the production of many songs with Jean Schwartz. He also wrote some music himself.

What Jolly Fun!

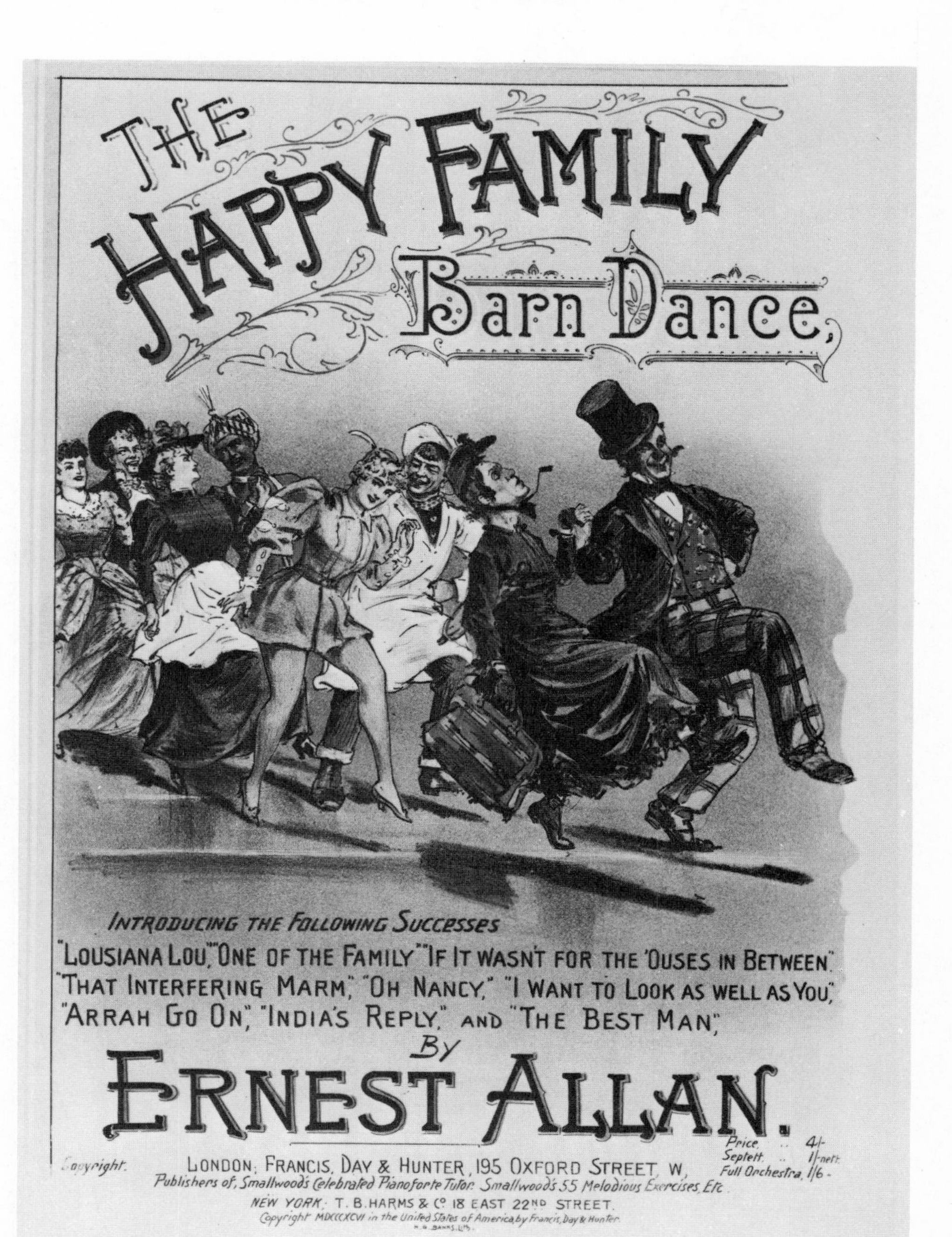

The Merry Little Fat Grey Man

Written and composed by JONATHAN BLEWITT

round as an ap - ple, and plump as a pear, He
has not a shill-ing, nor has he a care, He
lentando
has not a shill - ing, nor has he a care.
Yet he laughs and he sings, and he sings and he laughs, Yet he
laughs and he sings, and he sings and he laughs, And he laughs ha! ha! ha!

ha!
Laughs ha! ha! ha!
ha!
Ha!
ha!
ff
ad lib.
3
ha!
Ha!
ha!
ha! ha! ha! ha!
ha!
3
Oh! what a mer - ry mer - ry mer - ry mer - ry mer - ry mer - ry
p
lit - tle lit - tle lit - tle lit - tle lit - tle lit - tle lit - tle lit - tle
fat fat fat fat fat fat fat fat fat grey man.

The Merry Little Fat Grey Man

1. There is a little man dress'd all in grey,
He lives in the city, and he's always gay,
He lives in the city, and he's always gay;
He's round as an apple, and plump as a pear,
He has not a shilling, nor has he a care.

CHORUS: Yet he laughs and he sings, and he sings an
Yet he laughs and he sings, and he sings an
And he laughs ha! ha! ha! ha!
Laughs ha! ha! ha! ha!
Ha! ha! ha!
Ha! ha! ha! ha! ha! ha! ha!
O! what a merry merry merry merry merry
little little little little little little little littl
fat fat fat fat fat fat fat fat fat grey man.

2. He drinks without counting the number of glasses,
He sings merry songs and flirts with the lasses,
He sings merry songs and flirts with the lasses;
He has debts, he has duns, when the bailiffs draw nea
He shuts up his door and he shuts up his ear.

CHORUS: Yet he laughs and he sings, etc.

3. If the rain through the roof of his garret floor wets,
In his bed snoring snugly, the rain he forgets,
In his bed snoring snugly, the rain he forgets;
In bleak cold December, it hails and it snows,
If the fire goes out, his fingers he blows.

CHORUS: Yet he laughs and he sings, etc.

Apparently first of the genus of laughing songs, this was one of the fav
the entertainer and composer John L. Hatton who wrote 'Simon the Cell
was popularly supposed to be a skit on Hatton who was a tubby, jolly figu
of Jack Tar.

Musical interest lies in the accompaniment rather than in the vocal lin
words probably outstrip both. It is essentially a performer's song owin
parlour than to the concert platform.

Jonathan Blewitt (1780?–1853) was the son of the organist and son
Blewitt who educated him musically and in addition arranged for h
instruction from Haydn. Jonathan also became an organist, and wrote
Drury Lane which burned down before the production. After a spell as
Ireland he settled in London and began composing music for pantomim
tion that lasted him to the close of his life. At different times musical d
Theatre Royal Dublin, Sadlers Wells and Vauxhall Gardens, he compo
thousand songs, most of them comic. His end, however, was far from ar
died penniless after a most painful illness.

Simon the Cellarer

by W. H. BELLAMY

Composed by JOHN L. HATTON

Cy - prus, and who can say how ma - ny more! For a
cha - ry old soul is he, A cha - ry old soul is
he. Of Sack and Ca - na - ry he ne - ver doth fail, And
all the year round there is brew - ing of ale, Yet
ad lib.
he ne - ver ail - eth, he quaint - ly doth say, While he
col voce
sost.

p
keeps to his so - ber six fla - gons a day. But
p
ho! ho! ho! his nose doth shew How oft the black Jack to his
a tempo
f
lips doth go. But ho! ho! ho! his nose doth shew How
f
oft the black Jack to his lips doth go.
mf
f

Simon the Cellarer

1. Old Simon the cellarer keeps a large store,
   Of Malmsey and Malvoisie
   And Cyprus, and who can say how many more!
      For a chary old soul is he,
      A chary old soul is he.
   Of Sack and Canary he never doth fail,
   And all the year round there is brewing of ale,
   Yet he never aileth, he quaintly doth say,
   While he keeps to his sober six flagons a day.
         But ho! ho! ho! his nose doth shew
         How oft the black Jack to his lips doth go.
         But ho! ho! ho! his nose doth shew
         How oft the black Jack to his lips doth go.

2. Dame Margery sits in her own still-room,
   And a matron sage is she,
   From thence oft at Curfew is wafted a fume;
      She says it is Rosemarie,
      She says it is Rosemarie.
   But there's a small cupboard behind the back stair,
   And the maids say they often see Margery there—
   Now Margery says that she grows very old,
   And must take a something to keep out the cold!
         But ho! ho! ho! old Simon doth know,
         Where many a flask of his best doth go.
         But ho! ho! ho! old Simon doth know
         Where many a flask of his best doth go.

3. Old Simon reclines in his high back'd chair,
   And talks about taking a wife;
   And Margery often is heard to declare
      She ought to be settled in life,
      She ought to be settled in life.
   But Margery has (so the maids say) a tongue,
   And she's not very handsome, and not very young:
   So somehow it ends with a shake of the head,
   And Simon he brews him a tankard instead.
         While ho! ho! ho! He will chuckle and crow,
         What! marry old Margery? no, no, no!
         While ho! ho! ho! He will chuckle and crow,
         What! marry old Margery? no, no, no!

Despite a rather obvious lyric, this is an extremely singable piece that responds to a full-blooded performance. The whole song is pushed on by such subtleties as the 2–1 suspensions in 'But ho, ho, ho, etc.' A jaunty rhythm conjures up the gouty old vintner with his dot-and-carry gait. The ridiculous bird-calls in bars 21 to 23 add to the caricature as does the piano's final slightly tipsy remark. There is little wonder that it became the one great respectable comic song of Victorian England. The celebrated baritone Sir Charles Santley was noted for his magnificently ripe characterisation of Simon. Another comic song did service as a sequel; it was entitled 'Margery'.

W. H. Bellamy wrote a number of songs in the mid-century, including 'The Lady of the Lea' with music by Henry Smart.

Some notes on John Liptrot Hatton appear on page 26, but it should be remarked here that he was one of the few mid-Victorian entertainers, when comic songs were frowned upon by the genteel, to introduce comedy into his performances. It was, of course, very strait-laced comedy. He cannot have laughed much over the subsequent wide success of 'Simon' after he had parted with the copyright for a ten pound note.

Grandmother's Chair

Written and composed by JOHN READ

same un-to my sis-ter I de-clare, But when it came to me, the
cresc.
law-yer said, "I see, She has left to you her old arm chair."
CHORUS
mf
And how they tit-ter'd, how they chaff'd, How my bro-ther and
mf
sis - ter laugh'd, When they heard the law - yer de-clare,
3
Gran-ny had on - ly left to me her old arm chair.

Grandmother's Chair

1. My grandmother she at the age of eighty three
   One day in May was taken ill and died;
   And after she was dead, the will of course was read,
   By a lawyer as we all stood by his side;
   To my brother it was found, she had left a hundred pounds,
   The same unto my sister I declare,
   But when it came to me, the lawyer said, 'I see,
   She has left to you her old arm chair.'

CHORUS: And how they titter'd, how they chaff'd,
How my brother and sister laugh'd,
When they heard the lawyer declare,
Granny had only left to me her old arm chair.

2. I tho't it hardly fair, still I said I did not care,
   And in the ev'ning took the chair away;
   The neighbours they me chaff'd, my brother at me laugh'd
   And said, 'It will be useful, John, some day;
   When you settle down in life, find some girl to be your wife,
   You'll find it very handy I declare,
   On a cold and frosty night, when the fire is burning bright,
   You can then sit in your old arm chair.'

CHORUS: And how they titter'd, how they chaff'd, etc.

3. What my brother said was true, for in a year or two,
   Strange to say, I settled down in married life;
   I first a girl did court, and then the ring I bought,
   Took her to church, and when she was my wife,
   The old girl and me, were as happy as could be,
   For when my work was over I declare,
   I ne'er abroad would roam, but each night would stay at home,
   And be seated in my old arm chair.

CHORUS: And how they titter'd, how they chaff'd, etc.

4. One night the chair fell down, when I pick'd it up I found
   The seat had fallen out upon the floor;
   And there to my surprise I saw before my eyes,
   A lot of notes, two thousand pounds or more;
   When my brother heard of this, the fellow I confess,
   Went nearly mad with rage, and tore his hair.
   But I only laughed at him, then said unto him, 'Jem,
   Don't you wish you had the old arm chair?'

CHORUS: And how they titter'd, how they chaff'd, etc.

This sprightly little song with its irresistible chorus capitalises upon contemporary sentimentalia about chairs (see 'The Old Arm Chair', earlier in this volume), grandfather clocks and other items that reminded a million singers of lost loved ones. Despite its English origin, this piece was immensely popular in America—the version printed above comes from an early American edition—and has a lightness, ease and simplicity more closely allied to American composers like Henry Clay Work than to his British contemporaries.

John Read is a shadowy figure. He wrote and sang songs popular in the music-hall, among them 'Whoa, Emma' with T. S. Lonsdale.

Whist! the Bogie Man

Written by EDWARD HARRIGAN

Composed by DAVID BRAHAM

ta - ble, Up - set the dish and pan, I love to hear your
mo - ther say, Whist! whist! the bo - gie man! Oh, whist! whist!
CHORUS
whist! Here comes the bo - gie man, Now go to bed, you
ba - by, You Tom - my, Nell, and Dan; Oh, whist! whist!

Whist! the Bogie Man

Whist! The Bogie Man

1. Oh! gather round me, little ones,
   So full of fun and glee,
   Your father's going to be a fool,
   To plaze the famil*ee*;
   All jump upon the table,
   Upset the dish and pan,
   I love to hear your mother say,
   Whist! whist! the bogie man!

CHORUS: Oh, whist! whist! whist!
  Here comes the bogie man,
  Now go to bed, you baby,
  You Tommy, Nell, and Dan;
  Oh, whist! whist! whist!
  He'll catch ye, if he can;
  And all the popsey, wopseys wop
  Run from the bogie man.

2. When I sit down to dinner,
   It's seldom I have pie;
   If I must speak it's once a week,
   Then all the babies cry;
   It's with their little fingers,
   They dip into the pan,
   It's then I hear their mother cry
   Whist! whist! the bogie man!

CHORUS: Oh, whist! whist! whist! etc.

3. I hid out in the pantry,
   I hid out in the hall,
   To frighten all the little ones,
   I let the dishes fall;
   Then they began boo-hooing,
   Away, away they ran,
   'Twas then I heard their mother say,
   Whist! whist! the bogie man!

CHORUS: Oh, whist! whist! whist! etc.

4. Oh, when I meet an old-time friend
   Who's coming home quite late,
   I take a drop of rye and rock,
   And oysters on a plate;
   Oh, in the house I stumble,
   And wake up Nell and Dan,
   'Tis then I hear their mother say,
   Whist! whist! the bogie man!

CHORUS: Oh, whist! whist! whist! etc.

This lively glimpse of Irish domesticity in New York City comes from the Harrigan and Hart production of *The Mulligan Guards' Surprise* of February 1880. Like 'Maggie Murphy's Home', another Harrigan number printed in *The Parlour Song Book*, it brings a healthy breath of fresh air into the parlour: the situation is patently realistic, and any mawkishness is relieved by the frankness of the final verse. It has, all the same, much more charm than contemporary songs about home life emanating from the English music-hall.

The music is an unmistakable Irish jig and has some curious phrase lengths that could be said unkindly to owe their origin to the peat-bog rather than a city background. The delightfully odd lyric is reflected in the decidedly odd music. The English dance band leader, Henry Hall, who resurrected the song in the 1930s, felt constrained to force it between 4/4 bar lines and to rob it of much of its zaniness.

Edward or Ned Harrigan (1845–1911) was born in New York into an Irish family, son of a Canadian sea-captain, and grew up in the melting-pot of immigrant workers that was to provide him with so much material for his stage shows. He had a spell as a seaman and docker, and began acting as an amateur. He turned professional after meeting his handsome partner, Tony Hart, who was also of Irish origin and whose real name was Anthony Cannon (1855–1891). Hart's lively and varied talents stretched to utterly convincing female impersonation. Harrigan and Hart launched off as black-face Minstrels, formed a double act, 'The Nonpareils', and abandoned their burnt cork when they put on a musical sketch, 'The Mulligan Guard'. The music for this was written by Harrigan's father-in-law David Braham (1838–1905), an immigrant from England who played the violin in theatre orchestras and became a musical director for the stage. He had chosen the violin as his instrument while still a boy after finding the harp he was learning to play was too bulky to fit on a stage coach. 'The Mulligan Guard' was ludicrous enough and melodious enough to catch on famously. It was the starting point for the unique mixture of song, comedy sketch, dance, burlesque and other vaudeville elements, all based on the events of humble city life, that blossomed into a whole new genre of stage extravanganza. Usually exploiting an Irish theme, Harrigan and Hart would nonetheless poke fun at any racial minority with fine impartiality. They filled various New York theatres until the early 'nineties with many dozens of productions. After bitter rows Tony Hart left the partnership in 1885 and died six years later, but Ned Harrigan continued to whip his team along and, indeed, many of his best songs date from after the Hart period. The pace slackened as the 'nineties opened, and a last few shows were staged in the new century to apathetic audiences whose tastes had moved on to more sophisticated fare.

Thursday

Written by FRED E. WEATHERLY

Composed by JAMES L. MOLLOY

Thursday

rit.
bait so fine, And thus they sang in the e - ven - shine: "Oh! to-
rit.
-mor-row will be Fri-day, so we fish the stream to - day; Oh! to-
-mor-row will be_ Fri-day, so we fish the stream. Be-ne - di - ci-
- te."
2. So
down they sat by the riv - er's brim, And fished till the light was

grow - ing dim, They fish'd the stream till the moon was high, But
rit.
nev - er a fish came wand - 'ring by. They fish'd the stream in the
bright moon - shine, But not one fish would he come to dine; And the
Ab - bot said, "It seems to me, These ras - cal - ly fish are all gone to
rit.
sea, And to - mor - row will be Fri - day, but we've caught no fish to -
rit.

-day; Oh! to-mor-row will be__ Fri-day, but we've caught no fish. Mal-e-
-di - ci-te." 3. So back they went to the con-vent gate,
Ab-bot and monks dis-con - so-late, For they tho't of the mor-row with
lentando
fa - ces white, Say-ing, "Oh! we must curb our ap - pe-tite, But
suivez
down in the depths of the vaults be-low, There's Mal-voi-sie for a

world of woe"; So they quaff their wine and all de - clare That
fish, af - ter all, is but grue - some fare. "Oh! to - mor - row will be
rit.
rit.
rit.
rit.
Fri - day, so we'll warm our souls to - day; Oh! to - mor - row will be
Fri - day, so we'll warm our souls. Be - ne - di - ci - te".

Thursday

1. The sun was setting and vespers done,
   From chapel the monks came one by one,
   And down they went thro' the garden trim,
   In cassock and cowl, to the river's brim.
   Ev'ry brother his rod he took,
   Ev'ry rod had a line and hook,
   Ev'ry hook had a bait so fine,
   And thus they sang in the evenshine:
   'Oh! tomorrow will be Friday, so we fish the stream today;
   Oh! tomorrow will be Friday, so we fish the stream.
   Benedicite.'

2. So down they sat by the river's brim,
   And fished till the light was growing dim.
   They fish'd the stream till the moon was high,
   But never a fish came wand'ring by.
   They fish'd the stream in the bright moonshine,
   But not one fish would he come to dine;
   And the Abbot said, 'It seems to me,
   These rascally fish are all gone to sea,
   And tomorrow will be Friday, but we've caught no fish today;
   Oh! tomorrow will be Friday, but we've caught no fish.
   Maledicite.'

3. So back they went to the convent gate,
   Abbot and monks disconsolate,
   For they tho't of the morrow with faces white,
   Saying, 'Oh! we must curb our appetite,
   But down in the depths of the vaults below,
   There's Malvoisie for a world of woe;'
   So they quaff their wine and all declare
   That fish, after all, is but gruesome fare.
   'Oh! tomorrow will be Friday, so we'll warm our souls today;
   Oh! tomorrow will be Friday, so we'll warm our souls.
   Benedicite.'

Some nineteenth century painters, despite the prevailing nonconformist climate, had a fixation about monks and the Roman Catholic hierarchy. They were depicted as jolly old topers, quenching with enormous gusto their various appetites. Paintings of carousing cardinals and portly friars tucking into barons of beef were engraved and rolled off the presses in great numbers. There were a few songs in like vein: 'The Friar of Orders Grey' from early in the century is one, and 'Thursday' another. Whether or not there was any overt intention of discrediting the self-indulgent Romans in sober Victorian eyes, there is an unmistakable feeling of illicit enjoyment about this whole genre.

Molloy (see page 171) had a gift for easy melody and it is readily apparent in this piece. Weatherly (see page 180) is also at his best as a lyricist here. Incidentally, the line, 'Tomorrow will be Friday, but we've caught no fish today,' was a catch-phrase of the period, spoken or sung on every suitable occasion to expedite the laggard.

See Me Dance the Polka

Written and composed by GEORGE GROSSMITH

See Me Dance the Polka

round. When the band com - menc - es play - ing, My
feet be - gin to go, For a rol - lick - ing romp - ing
Pol - ka, Is the jol - li - est fun I know.
f
sf

See Me Dance the Polka

1. A fig for the set of Lancers,
A fig for the old Quadrille,
They may suit some kind of dancers,
But their dullness makes me ill;
A fig for the stately waltzing,
Which really is absurd;
On the smart Cotillion, unsuited to the million,
I will not waste a word.
You should see me dance the Polka,
You should see me cover the ground,
You should see my coat-tails flying,
As I jump my partner round;
When the band commences playing,
My feet begin to go,
For a rollicking romping Polka,
Is the jolliest fun I know.

2. I've danced it in the Ball room,
And then would dance it still;
I've danced it in a small room,
I've danced it on the hill.
With every kind of partner,
In every kind of hall,
I've even had to suffer, by dancing with a duffer
Who couldn't do the step at all.
You should see me dance the Polka,
You should see me cover the ground,
You should see my coat-tails flying,
As I jump my partner round;
When the band commences playing,
My feet begin to go,
For a rollicking romping Polka,
Is the jolliest fun I know.

3. I know I'm rather active,
And not devoid of grace,
But still I'm unattractive,
In feature, form, and face;
I have a simple fortune,
And lead a simple life,
You know what an old maid is? Well fourteen of those ladies
Offered to be my wife.
They saw me dance the Polka,
They saw me cover the ground
They saw my coat-tails flying,
As I jumped my partner round.
When the band commences playing,
My feet begin to go,
For a rollicking romping Polka
Is the jolliest fun I know.

4. One of my rich relations
Was very fond of me,
From him I'd expectations,
In form of a legacy.
I calculated surely,
On a house and an acre or two,
So I went and got married, but my hopes miscarried,
And what was I to do?
He left me a copy of a polka,
And on the cover I found
A sketch of my coat-tails flying,
As I jumped my partners round.
When the band commences playing,
My feet begin to go,
For a rollicking romping Polka
Is the jolliest fun I know.

To be sung a little slower, in rather a quavery voice.

5. But now I'm old and shaky,
My back is bent, you see,
My limbs are rather quaky,
And scarcely bear with me.
I'm never asked to dances,
I'm placed upon the shelf
But altho' I'm rheumatic, still as long as I've an attic,
I'll dance it by myself.
You shall see me dance the polka,
You shall see me cover the ground,
You shall see my coat-tails flying,
As I hobble myself around.
If I hear an organ playing,
So long as my strength don't give,
I'll dance that rollicking polka,
The longest day I live.

Her Majesty Queen Victoria, it is pleasant to record, was amused. She even requested an encore. Undoubtably, she could hardly not tap an august toe with the syncopation on the hop of the polka. It is a masterstroke.

George Grossmith (1847–1912) was an entertainer of such popularity that he was able to appeal to all levels of society and delight royalty as much as the music-hall gallery. In boyhood he amused his friends with comic songs at the piano, and later, in intervals from his job as a deputy police-court reporter for his journalist father, he developed his amiable talent. Eventually he became a professional artiste, and rose to join the great team mustered by Richard D'Oyly Carte to delight England with the Gilbert and Sullivan operettas. He created such roles as the Lord Chancellor in *Iolanthe*, admirably suited to his witty, pointed style, at its best in patter songs. A small, dry man, he could reduce his audiences to tears with his inoffensive jocularity. Together with his brother, Weedon, he wrote that classic saga of suburban gentility, *The Diary of a Nobody*.

Two's Company

A Selection of Duets

Believe Me, If All Those Endearing Young Charms

Written by THOMAS MOORE, music traditional

- dear-ing young charms, Which I gaze on so fond - ly to - day, Were to
all those young charms, Which I gaze on so fond - ly to - day,
change by to - mor - row, and fleet in my arms, Like
Were to change and fleet in my arms, Like
fai - ry gifts fad - ing a - way, Thou wouldst still be a - dor'd as this
fai - ry gifts fad - ing a - way, Thou wouldst still be a - dor'd as this

mo-ment thou art, Let thy love - li - ness fade as it will; And a -
mo-ment thou art, Let thy love - li - ness fade as it will; And a -
- round the dear ru - in each wish of my heart Would en -
- round the dear ru - in each wish of my heart Would en -
- twine it - self ver - dant-ly still.
- twine it - self ver - dant-ly still.
mf
ri - tard.

Believe Me, If All Those Endearing Young Charms

1. Believe me, if all those endearing young charms,
   Which I gaze on so fondly today,
   Were to change, by tomorrow, and fleet in my arms,
   Like fairy gifts fading away,
   Thou would'st still be ador'd as this moment thou art,
   Let thy loveliness fade as it will;
   And around the dear ruin each wish of my heart
   Would entwine itself verdantly still.

2. It is not while beauty and youth are thine own,
   And thy cheeks unprofan'd by a tear,
   That the fervour and faith of a soul can be known,
   To which time will but make thee more dear!
   Oh, the heart that has truly loved never forgets,
   But as truly loves on to the close!
   As the sunflower turns on her god when he sets,
   The same look which she turn'd when he rose.

One of Thomas Moore's *Irish Melodies* in a duet setting, this has an ingenuous and sweet tune to which the sophisticated *ritornello* pays elegant court. It is a superb piece for two well-balanced youthful voices. The origin of the melody is the folk-song 'My Lodging is on the Cold Ground', which was possibly originally English rather than Irish. It had at one time words written for it by Sir William Davenant and an arrangement by, perhaps, Matthew Locke. In 1836 the tune was borrowed again and appeared in cap and gown as 'Fair Harvard' to celebrate the jubilee of that foundation.

What Are the Wild Waves Saying?

Written by J. E. Carpenter

Composed by Stephen Glover

Andante *con espressione*

p

cresc. *dim. ritard.* *p*

a tempo

PAUL

1. What are the wild waves saying, Sister, the whole day long, That

e - ver a-mid our play - ing I hear but their low, lone
Animato
cresc.
song? Not by the sea - side on - ly,
cresc.
dol
There, it sounds wild and free; But at night, when 'tis dark and
3
cresc.
f
dim.
p
lone - ly, In dreams it is still with me, But at
night, when 'tis dark and lone - ly, In dreams it is still with

Più animato
FLORENCE
me.
Bro-ther, I hear no sing - ing!
dim.
p
'Tis but the rol - ling wave,
E-ver its lone course
wing - ing
O - ver some o - cean cave!
Agitato
'Tis but the noise of wa - ter
Dash-ing a - gainst the
cre - scen - do
f
shore,
And the wind, from some bleak - er quar - ter,

Ming - ling with its roar, And the wind, from some bleak - er
f
quart - er, Ming - ling, ming - ling with its roar.
ritard.
tremolo
p
FLORENCE
Lento
rall. a tempo
No! no, no, no! No, no, no, it is some - thing
PAUL
No! no, no, no! No, no, no, it is some - thing
Lento
rall.
p
great - er That speaks to the heart a -
great - er That speaks to the heart a -

-lone, The voice of the great Cre - a - - tor
-lone, The voice of the great Cre - a - - tor
Dwells in that migh-ty tone! The voice of the great Cre -
Dwells in that migh-ty tone! The voice of the great Cre -
rall.
3
- a - - tor Dwells in that migh-ty tone!
3
- a - - tor Dwells in that migh-ty tone!
rall.
sf
cresc.
f
p

What Are the Wild Waves Saying?

- way?
Is it a friend - ly greet - ing? Or a
warn - ing that calls a - way?
FLORENCE
Più animato
Bro-ther! the in - land
dim.
p
moun-tain Hath it not voice and sound? Speaks not the drip-ping
foun-tain As it be-dews the ground?
Agitato
E'en by the household
cre - - - scen -
in - - gle, Cur-tain'd and closed and warm,
- - do
f

What Are the Wild Waves Saying?

- lone, The voice of the great Cre - a - - tor . . .
- lone, The voice of the great Cre - a - - tor . . .
Dwells in that migh-ty tone! The voice of the great Cre -
Dwells in that migh - ty tone! The voice of the great Cre-
rall.
- a - - tor . . . Dwells in that migh-ty tone!
- a - - tor . . . Dwells in that migh - ty tone!
rall.
sf
cresc.
f
p

What Are the Wild Waves Saying?

1. PAUL: What are the wild waves saying,
Sister, the whole day long,
That ever amid our playing
I hear but their low, lone song?
Not by the seaside only,
There, it sounds wild and free;
But at night, when 'tis dark and lonely,
In dreams it is still with me,
But at night, when 'tis dark and lonely,
In dreams it is still with me.

FLORENCE: Brother, I hear no singing!
'Tis but the rolling wave,
Ever its lone course winging
Over some ocean cave!
'Tis but the noise of water
Dashing against the shore,
And the wind, from some bleaker quarter,
Mingling with its roar,
And the wind, from some bleaker quarter,
Mingling, mingling with its roar.

FLORENCE AND PAUL: No! no, no, no!
No, no, no, it is something greater
That speaks to the heart alone,
The voice of the great Creator
Dwells in that mighty tone!
The voice of the great Creator
Dwells in that mighty tone!

2. PAUL: Yes! but the waves seem ever
Singing the same sad thing,
And vain is my weak endeavour,
To guess what the surges sing.
What is that voice repeating,
Ever by night and day?
Is it a friendly greeting?
Or a warning that calls away?
Is it a friendly greeting?
Or a warning that calls away?

FLORENCE: Brother! the inland mountain
Hath it not voice and sound?
Speaks not the dripping fountain
As it bedews the ground?
E'en by the household ingle,
Curtain'd and closed and warm,
Do not our voices mingle
With those of the distant storm?
Do not our voices mingle
With those of the distant, distant storm?

FLORENCE AND PAUL: Yes! yes, yes!
Yes! yes, but there's something greater
That speaks to the heart alone,
The voice of the great Creator
Dwells in that mighty tone!
The voice of the great Creator
Dwells in that mighty tone!

Like such other songs as 'The Ivy Green' and 'Little Nell', this piece was inspired by an incident in a novel by Charles Dickens. Early in *Dombey and Son* the reader is introduced to poor Paul, the little, ailing, motherless son of the stern and prosperous merchant Mr Paul Dombey senior. The boy is sent to the seaside at Brighton for his health, and is tended by his gentle sister Florence, neglected by her father because he wanted his first child to be a son. Paul is wheeled in a little carriage to 'the margin of the ocean' every day, and on one occasion:

> ... he fell asleep, and slept quietly for a long time. Awakening suddenly, he listened, started up, and sat listening.
>
> Florence asked him what he thought he heard.
>
> 'I want to know what it says,' he answered, looking steadily in her face. 'The sea, Floy, what is it that it keeps on saying?'
>
> She told him it was only the noise of the rolling waves.
>
> 'Yes, yes,' he said. 'But I know that they are always saying something. Always the same thing. What place is over there?' He rose up, looking eagerly at the horizon.
>
> She told him that there was another country opposite, but he said he didn't mean that: he meant farther away—farther away!
>
> Very often afterwards, in the midst of their talk, he would break off, to try to understand what it was the waves were always saying; and would rise up in his couch to look towards that invisible region, far away.

No Victorian reader could fail to comprehend the imagery. The duet is a dialogue between Paul and Florence, attributing to them an understanding of the deeper things of life that Dickens unaccountably omitted to include in the story. Paul was marked to die, and his deathbed scene is protracted and pathetic: 'I hear the waves', he whispers, and passes over to where his dead mama waits for him on the other shore.

The lyric of this song is pretty fustian stuff and no great credit to its author Joseph Edwardes Carpenter who was also responsible for 'Her Bright Smile Haunts Me Still' and 'The Goodbye at the Door', both set to music by Stephen Glover, and for 'Do They Think of Me at Home?' composed by Stephen's brother, C. W. Glover. The setting of 'What Are the Wild Waves Saying?' is a good deal better than the words. Paul's music is bound up with sea sounds with arpeggios representing the waves, while Florence is squarely on land. In the duet passages, however, the sea figure takes over as they both realise that Paul is right: it is the voice of the great Creator. Agitation is expressed in a broken staccato accompaniment.

Stephen Ralph Glover (1813–1870) was one of the most fertile of English ballad writers. He produced nearly fifteen hundred compositions: songs both secular and sacred, duets, pieces for the piano and a chamber opera. 'What Are the Wild Waves Saying?' is his most famous piece. His brother Charles W. Glover composed 'The Rose of Tralee' on page 203. There was also another musical Glover of the period, William Howard Glover (1819–1875), a far more serious character than the songwriting brothers. Teacher, violinist, conductor and composer of operettas, he spent much of his life in the United States.

O That We Two Were Maying

Written by the Rev. Charles Kingsley   Composed by Alice Mary Smith

stream __ of the soft _ spring breeze, Like _ chil - dren with vio-lets play - ing In _ the
stream __ of the soft _ spring breeze, Like _ chil - dren with vio-lets play - ing In the
shade ____ of the whisp'-ring trees.
shade ____ of the whisp'-ring trees. O ______ that we two _ were
p
p
cresc.
O ______ that we two _ were may - ing O ______ that we two _ were
may - ing O ______ that we two _ were may - ing

may - ing In the shade of the whisp'-ring trees.
O that we two were maying A-mong the whisp'-ring trees.
O that we two sat dream - ing On the sward of some sheep-trimm'd
p
down Watch - - ing the white mist steal - ing O - -
- - ver ri - ver mead and town.
p
O that we two sat

dream - ing,
O that we two sat dream - ing
cresc.
dim.
O that we two sat dream - ing, On the sward of some
cresc.
dim.
down.
O that we two sat dream - ing, sat dream -
pp
colla voce
- - - ing,
that
pp
we,
O that
O that we two were may - ing, Down the
morendo

we were may - ing, Like chil - dren with vio - lets
stream of the soft spring breeze, Like chil - dren with vio - lets
play - ing In the shade of the whisp'ring trees.
play - ing In the shade of the whisp'ring trees.
O that we two were may - ing Down the stream of the soft spring
O that we two were may - ing Down the stream of the soft spring

breeze, Like chil - dren with vio - lets play - ing In the
breeze, Like chil - dren with vio lets play - ing In the
shade of the whisp'ring trees O that
shade of the whisp'ring trees O that we two were
we were may - - ing
may - ing O that we two were may - ing

O that we were may - - - -
O that we were may - -
- ing, may - - ing,
- ing, may - - ing,
may - - ing.
may - - - ing.

O That We Two Were Maying

O that we two were maying
  Down the stream of the soft spring breeze,
Like children with violets playing
  In the shade of the whisp'ring trees.

O that we two sat dreaming
  On the sward of some sheep-trimm'd down
Watching the white mist stealing
  Over river mead and town.

Compared to the earnest doggerel of the preceding song, Charles Kingsley's simple lyric looks like genuine poetry. It is, in fact, completely in the idealistic taste of the time and may be compared to those atmospheric oleographs of country lanes at dusk so beloved by our forefathers. The setting has a fine pastoral rhythm supporting lines of sustained and beautiful melody: an accomplished piece of writing completely in key with the verse. Another setting also exists, by the American composer Ethelbert Nevin who wrote the sugary 'Mighty Lak' a Rose' and the art ballad 'The Rosary' included in *The Parlour Song Book.*

Like Longfellow, Kingsley possessed the type of inspiration particularly appreciated in the parlour, and composers vied to set his latest offerings. Omitted from this song is the last verse of his poem, which begins:

O that we two were sleeping
  In our nest in the churchyard sod. . .

Notes on Kingsley may be found on page 73, with his song 'Three Fishers Went Sailing'.

Alice Mary Smith (Mrs Meadows White, 1839–1884) was a minor English lady composer highly regarded by the upper middle classes. She studied under Sir W. Sterndale Bennett and Sir G. A. Macfarran and married a lawyer who subsequently became a judge. She was honoured by her election as Female Professional Associate of the Philharmonic Society and Honorary Member of the Royal Academy of Music. Her many works include symphonies, overtures, a clarinet concerto, other orchestral pieces, chamber music, cantatas, part-songs, duets and ballads. Truly respectable, in all senses of the word.

The Battle Eve

Written by ROBERT SOUTHEY

Composed by THEO BONHEUR

Andante moderato

p

p BASS

1. Dark the shades of night are grow - ing, Keen and chill the wind is blow - ing, Bright the watchfire lights are glow - ing,

p

dim. 'Tis the bat-tle eve, *rall.* 'Tis the bat-tle

dim. *rall.*

TENOR
a tempo
Ah! the shades of night tomorrow
eve! Ah! the shades of night tomorrow
Will to many bring a sorrow; But of that we
cresc.
will not borrow On this battle eve.

rall.
cresc.
f
On this bat-tle eve. A - way! A - way! A - way!
rall.
cresc.
f
On this bat-tle eve. A - way! A - way! A - way!
rall.
f
Tempo di marcia
f
A - way, a-way, with hearts so gay, A - way, we'll go to fight the
f
A - way, a-way, with hearts so gay, A - way, we'll go to fight the
Tempo di marcia
f marcato
3
foe; At dawn of day we'll to the fray, And
foe, We'll go to fight the foe; At dawn of day we'll to the fray, And
3

ff
strive to lay our ri - vals low, And strive to__ lay our__ ri - vals
ff
strive to lay our ri - vals low, And strive to__ lay our__ ri - vals
ff
low.
low.
1st time
1st time
marcato
2nd time
2nd time
3
rall.
D.S.

Tempo di marcia
mf
3. Hark! the bug - le, loud - ly call - ing, Sounds to one and all en -
3. Hark! the bug - le, loud - ly call - ing, Sounds to one and all en -
Tempo di marcia
mf con spirito
thrall - ing; List! the sound of drums is fall - ing,
thrall - ing; List! the sound of drums is fall - ing,
marcato
'Tis the dawn of day! Now to arms, the call, make
ff
'Tis the dawn of day! Now to arms, Now to arms, the call, make
3

rea - dy, Now we march so firm and stea - dy, Now we
rea - dy, Now we march so firm and stea - dy, Now we
ff
rush like whirl-ing, whirl-ing ed - dy, 'Tis the dawn of day!
rall.
rush like whirl-ing whirl-ing, ed - dy, 'Tis the dawn of day!
'Tis the dawn of day! A - way! A - way! A -
accel.
f
'Tis the dawn of day! A - way! A - way! A -
ff accel.

ff
rall.
- way! A - way! A-way! A - way! A -
ff
rall.
- way! A - way! way! A - way! A -
ff
rall.
Tempo di marcia
- way, a-way, with hearts so gay, A - way we go to fight the
- way, a-way, with hearts so gay, A - way we go to fight the
Tempo di marcia
f morendo
foe; 'Tis dawn of day, and to the fray, We
ff
foe We go to fight the foe; 'Tis dawn of day, and to the fray, We

ff
swift - ly go, with blow for blow, We swift - ly __ go, with _ blow for
ff
swift - ly go, with blow for blow, We swift - ly __ go, with _ blow for
ff
blow. ______ A - way! A-way! A - way! A-way! 'Tis the dawn of
rit.
blow. ______ A - way! A-way! A - way! A-way! 'Tis the dawn of
rit.
3
rit.
ff
day! 'Tis the dawn __ of day! ______
ff
day! 'Tis the dawn __ of day! ______
ff
marcato

The Battle Eve

1. Dark the shades of night are growing,
Keen and chill the wind is blowing,
Bright the watchfire lights are glowing,
'Tis the battle eve!

Ah! the shades of night tomorrow
Will to many bring a sorrow;
But of that we will not borrow
On this battle eve!

Away, away, with hearts so gay,
Away, we'll go to fight the foe;
At dawn of day we'll to the fray,
And strive to lay our rivals low.

2. See! our comrades there are sleeping,
While our lonesome watch we're keeping;
Little recking friends will weeping
Be tomorrow eve.

See! the dawn is now approaching,
Softly, silently encroaching;
O'er the field the day is broaching,
Gone is now the eve!

Away, away, with hearts so gay,
Away, we'll go to fight the foe;
At dawn of day we'll to the fray,
And strive to lay our rivals low.

3. Hark! the bugle, loudly calling,
Sounds to one and all enthralling;
List! the sound of drums is falling,
'Tis the dawn of day!

Now to arms, the call, make ready,
Now we march so firm and steady,
Now we rush like whirling eddy,
'Tis the dawn of day!

Away, away, with hearts so gay,
Away, we go to fight the foe;
'Tis dawn of day, and to the fray,
We swiftly go, with blow for blow.

Away! Away! Away! Away!
'Tis the dawn of day!

Harmonically and melodically ingenuous as it is, 'The Battle Eve' was suffiently martial and dramatic to make it a firm favourite in late Victorian drawing rooms. It seems to have a distinct feeling of Offenbach about certain passages.

Robert Southey (1774–1843), the English romantic poet and historian, was the son of a Bristol linen-draper. He was writing classical epics by the age of ten. Sent to school at Westminster, he was expelled for protesting against flogging which was well-known to be essential to the education of an English gentleman. Up at Oxford he said he studied only swimming and boating. He met Coleridge and fell under his unitarian and pantisocratic sway. Marriage to Elizabeth Fricker whose sister was to marry Coleridge, and a quarrel with that worthy, began to turn Southey away from his revolutionary ideas. He tried to study law, failed, and took up literary pursuits, supporting the Coleridge family as well as his own by his pen. This resulted in quantity rather than quality, especially in his historical works. A friendship with Sir Walter Scott led to the Poet Laureateship, and Southey's views took a further turn to the right. For the rest of his life he became increasingly bigoted and intolerant until softening of the brain killed him. Only a handful of his verses are read today, among them such parlour recitations as 'The Inchcape Rock' and 'The Battle of Blenheim'.

'Theo Bonheur' was the pseudonym of Alfred Rawlings (1857–?) who composed both instrumental music and songs, among them 'The King's Own' and 'The Boys are Marching'.

Index

TITLES

The entries in bold type indicate the beginning of the song

FIRST LINES

POETS AND COMPOSERS

The main entries are in bold type: these refer to the notes following a song written by the poet or composer